Acid Test

Forthcoming Books in the Test Trilogy

Mission Test
Zion Test

Acid Test

LSD vs. LDS

Christopher Kimball Bigelow

ZARAHEMLA BOOKS

Cover design by Jason Robinson
Interior book design and layout by Marny K. Parkin

Paperback ISBN 978-0-9993472-3-2
Hardcover ISBN 978-0-9993472-4-9
eBook ISBN 978-0-9993472-5-6

Published by Zarahemla Books
Provo, Utah, U.S.A.
info@zarahemlabooks.com
ZarahemlaBooks.com

"All people who have led hazardous and forbidden lives are, in a certain sense, imaginative; if their imaginations are not filled with good things, they will choke them for themselves with bad ones."

—Charles Dickens

"There is this quality, in things, of the right way seeming wrong at first."

—John Updike

"By proving contraries, truth is made manifest."

—Joseph Smith

Acid Test playlist: tinyurl.com/y62yaf6y

Part 1

"Don't know what I want, but I know how to get it."
—Sex Pistols, "Anarchy in the U.K."

"To fall in hell or soar angelic, you'll need a pinch of psychedelic."
—Humphry Osmond

Chapter 1

ONE EVENING IN MAY 1984, I DECIDED TO GO ALL THE way new wave. I was standing in the greasy, floury kitchen of a Kentucky Fried Chicken in Woods Cross, Utah. Pressure-fryer burns striped my forearms. A paste of eleven herbs and spices smeared my uniform and clogged my nostrils. I could feel my acne flaring like fanned coals. My hourly wage was $3.85, up fifty cents from when I'd started a year earlier.

Standing near the walk-in cooler, the night manager watched me load a birdcage-shaped rack with raw, battered chicken just starting to smell sweet with spoilage. A clean-cut Hispanic guy, he wore a new brown polyester uniform that didn't show any grease or flour. He'd recently returned home from a Mormon mission to Guatemala. Sometimes he still acted like a programmed android.

The radio started playing a ZZ Top song.

"Come on, turn it to 105.5," I asked again. KCGL was a new station that played alternative music I hadn't known existed until recently.

"Last night you were fine with Rock 103," the manager said.

"Yeah, and now it's my turn."

"What *is* this new-wave stuff, anyway?"

I shrugged. New wave wasn't a tidy category like disco or country. Before KCGL, I'd loved some music without realizing it was new wave—the Cars, the Police, and one-offs like Gary Numan, Soft Cell, M, and the Knack. Now I considered music authentically new wave only if KCGL played it, though KCGL called it modern music instead of new wave. Their playlist ranged from broody, British-sounding synthesizer bands like Depeche Mode to bizarre, punchy guitar bands like Oingo Boingo. New wave also included some reggae and rockabilly, which I disliked; some ska, which I liked; and punk, which mesmerized me. Hardcore punk bands like Suicidal Tendencies and Black Flag played the fastest, angriest music I'd ever heard.

I felt a crazy impulse. "I'll sell you my Van Halen ticket."

"Are you serious?" The manager stepped toward me. Van Halen's *1984* tour stop in Salt Lake was sold out. "How much?"

"Same as I paid, if I get my share of radio time."

"Done," he said.

I found it odd that a returned missionary was interested in rock. Interrupting the ZZ Top song, he skipped over a country station and landed on Romeo Void's "Never Say Never." I loved the song's new-wave decadence—*I might like you better if we slept together.* I hoped it bugged the clueless manager. I wasn't going to get sucked into serving a mission like he had.

During my senior year, I'd split myself between two groups of friends. One group was mostly Mormon guys who quoted Monty Python too much. We attended rock concerts in the smoke-filled Salt Palace, bands like Journey, Styx, April Wine, and—my favorite—Rush. My newer friends were mostly non-Mormon preppies who were turning into new wavers. They'd invited me to an upcoming Modern English show.

I knew Van Halen would be more entertaining than Modern English, one of the tamer new-wave bands. But this was about more than just a concert. Mainstream rock would never take me anywhere unusual or unexpected. But new wave was the gateway into a spiky-haired, clove-scented, underground scene.

With beer, blankets, and a battery-heavy boom box, seven of us hiked up Mueller Park Canyon, a few miles from my parents' house on the Bountiful bench. Lisa led the way with her flashlight. It was early August of 1984. Two months earlier, most of us had graduated from high school, and now it was our turn to fight Big Brother. To me, nothing was more Big Brother–ish than the LDS church.

The path was familiar to me. Hiking with Boy Scouts once, I'd seen a porn magazine lying on the dirt trail, splayed open like a beaver trap. Stumbling across porn was even better than finding money. Running ahead, I snagged the magazine, but the scoutmaster grabbed it from me and tucked it into his back pocket. We thought he'd burn it in our campfire, but he'd stowed it in the trunk of his car.

Leaving the trail, we followed Lisa across a creek and pushed deeper into the dark woods. In a clearing, we helped her build a fire. The clove fumes from our Indonesian cigarettes added exotic sweetness to the woodsmoke. Lisa's boom box played X's *Under the Big Black Sun*, which was old-school L.A. punk, not the newer hardcore punk. When "Blue Spark" came on, I stood up and played air guitar.

Chad sat next to me on a log, a brown paper bag tucked under his knees. More preppy than new wave, Chad kept his dark-brown hair in a tight 1950s-style flattop. He was a year younger than most of us. Chad's mom was semi-active in Mormonism, but Chad and his dad didn't attend. He was a major scammer, always looking for new girls. Part of me wished I could scam like that, but part of me thought it was gross.

"All right, Biggs." Chad pulled a bottle of clear liquor from the bag. I liked it when he called me Biggs. *Christopher* had too many syllables, and *Chris* was too androgynous. "Let's see what you're like drunk."

The others whooped and clapped. To steel myself, I dragged hard on my cigarette, making bits of clove crackle fragrantly. Earlier that week, in the basement Pie Pizzeria near the University of Utah, Chad had coaxed me to inhale my smoke instead of just mouthing it. My first nicotine buzz had felt almost as good as an orgasm. I'd finally understood why people got hooked on smoking.

Moving fast and efficiently like a paramedic, Chad unscrewed the bottle and handed it to me. Then he cracked open a beer and put it in my other hand.

"Give that booze a sniff," he said.

I sniffed. The liquor had an evergreen scent, appropriate for the forest setting. I wondered how bad it would taste.

"It's gin," Chad said. He told me to sip from the bottle and chase it with the beer. As I raised the bottle, I felt like I was getting initiated into a cult. The gin made me gag, but the beer helped.

"Wow," I said. "I guess this makes me not Mormon anymore." I felt free and relieved—I'd wanted this status since I was thirteen or so.

"Again," Chad pushed.

I was the last person in our group to drink, but I was the first to move out, though I was still only seventeen. A few days earlier, I'd moved into a crummy studio apartment near the U with a prelaw student named Virgil. Now I was free to do whatever I wanted. I didn't have to worry about hurting my mom or upsetting my dad. I didn't have to bother with Mormonism's bland, irrelevant busywork anymore.

☯

Swaying backward, I fell off my log. I tried to get up, but internal g-forces held me down, like on the spinning funhouse ride at Lagoon. Laughing, Chad got me reseated. I resumed sipping gin, no longer needing to chase with beer. I liked how warm and buzzy it made me feel.

Lisa kept the music rotating. In addition to X, our group's most sacred music included *What Is Beat?* by the English Beat, *The Hurting* by Tears for Fears, *Upstairs at Eric's* by Yaz, and the first three albums by the B-52s. If one band defined our group, it was the wacky B-52s. We loved their retro kitsch, their zany outer-space themes, and the two women's outrageous bouffants.

Lisa had graduated a year earlier. Instead of college, she now did data entry. Her mouse-brown hair was bushy and kinky, and she wore thick-framed eyeglasses, corduroy pants, polo shirts, and L.L. Bean duck shoes. She didn't use makeup or shave her legs or armpits. Due to a medical problem, she could never have children. She wasn't Mormon, but her older brother had converted and served a mission. When Susan Sarandon and Catherine Deneuve kissed in the vampire movie *The Hunger*, Lisa had stood up and clapped in a full theater.

Matt was my best friend in the group. His glossy black hair was buzzed except for thick, long bangs that flipped around. He wore a stud in his left ear, and he was good at mixing thrift-shop clothes with an occasional Nordstrom splurge. Matt was bisexual. He usually had a girlfriend, but sometimes he made eye contact with anonymous males in Salt Lake's two downtown malls. After disappearing for a while, he'd return with flushed cheeks and a sly smile. At Woods Cross High, he was known as Boner Boy for getting aroused once in the gym showers.

Matt lived with his mom and four younger siblings in the flatlands between the freeway and the Great Salt Lake, not far from an oil refinery. His dad was raised in a polygamous cult called the Work but later left it. Matt grew up in the normal

Mormon church until one day his dad arrived home from work and climbed onto the roof with a chainsaw, even though it was just starting to drizzle outside. He'd decided to add on another bedroom for his new second wife.

Janet and Vince sat on the same log. I could tell she liked him more than he liked her. Janet was from Clearfield, up north by the Air Force base. To escape her abusive stepfather, she'd lived in Bountiful for a year with ultra-Mormon relatives, and now she bounced from couch to couch, mostly with downtown punkers. Vince was a punk from Rose Park. He wore combat boots and a black trench coat, with the sides of his head shaved bald. I'd heard he could somehow put LSD directly into his eyeballs.

Matt had a new girl with him tonight. Tina was from Kearns out in the Salt Lake Valley. She sat pressed against him, a blanket around her bare shoulders. She wore orange short-shorts and a yellow tank top with no bra, but her breasts were smallish, without visible nipples. Her hair was honey blonde, and she seemed a little ditzy, more California valley girl than new waver. Whenever she giggled, her eyes crinkled almost shut. I didn't know if she were Mormon or not.

At one point, I heard myself slur, "I've never kissed a girl." Moments later, Tina stood before me, smiling. Lowering her face, she pressed her lips to mine. The points of her bob tickled my face, and I caught a whiff of lemongrass. Right before she broke off, I felt a thrilling tongue flicker. Giggling, she backed away, and I fell off my log again.

I woke achy on the floor of the second wife's bedroom, which was now Matt's room. I didn't mind the discomfort—I felt proud to have my first hangover, not regretful or guilty. After Tina's kiss, my only memory was stumbling back across the cold creek. Someone had pulled off my wet socks and pants and put a sheet over me.

It was after 10:00 a.m. Across the room, Janet slept on a towel in just her panties and bra. As I lay there, I could hear Matt's younger siblings downstairs. His mom worked, so he watched them during the summer. He'd missed junior high because he'd been forced to homeschool them. After three years, his mom had finally kicked out the husband, his second wife, and their two babies.

I smelled bacon, unsure if it made me feel hungrier or queasier. I wondered if other friends were downstairs with Matt. I hoped Tina was there, but she was only sixteen, so she'd probably gone home. Part of me wished Tina could be my reward for finally doing what I wanted instead of what my parents dictated. But I knew I'd need more confidence and courage if I was going to get her. Anyway, she was Matt's.

In all my teen years, I'd never had a girlfriend. But I'd told a fib as we sat around the fire. Tina was not technically my first kiss. Growing up in Los Angeles, I'd fallen in love with a girl named Patricia when we were both about eight. Her family was Mormon, all with thick brown hair and bright white teeth like the Osmonds. They lived in a sun-filled, high-ceilinged mansion way up in Rolling Hills Estates. Once, I saw Mike Lookinland at a party at their house, the Mormon kid who'd played Bobby Brady on TV.

In the backseat of her parents' Mercedes, Patricia taught me a secret clapping code, spelling out "I love you" to each other. One afternoon, she pulled me into a guest bathroom and flipped off the light. "Let's kiss like the movie stars do," she whispered in my ear. We kissed for a moment, not otherwise touching. Just when I thought we were getting going, she turned the light back on.

One night at my house, our parents wanted to stay up late without kids around. Compared to Patricia's mansion, our cookie-cutter tract home seemed poor—we were on the wrong side of Hawthorne Boulevard, down the hill in Rancho Palos Verdes, where a tidal wave might reach. Our parents tucked Patricia and me together into my top bunk. I wanted to hug and kiss in our pajamas, but I needed Patricia to start it. However, she just went right to sleep, or pretended to. A few weeks later at a church breakfast, I watched as she chased another boy. He was tall and sportsy, with curly dark hair. In comparison, I was a blond-headed bookworm.

Since that time, I'd been waiting for another Patricia. When I was four, I'd thought the Carpenters song "Close to You" was about me, but besides Patricia it didn't come true. After her, most of my crushes were on girls with brown hair and brown eyes, including actresses like Melissa Gilbert in *Little House on the Prairie*, Carrie Fisher in *Star Wars,* and Lady Aberlin on *Mister Rogers' Neighborhood*. While I was willing to stare at girls, I needed them to make the first move, but none ever did. In seventh grade, one girl even told me to stop staring at her. A couple of tomboys came after me, but I didn't like them. Meanwhile, ten years went by without another girlfriend.

I wondered if the next Patricia had finally kissed me.

Chapter 2

A FEW WEEKS AFTER I MOVED OUT, I INVITED MY DAD to buy me lunch. Every time I'd visited home, he'd asked me about my LDS church activity. I decided I'd rather tell him the truth in a public restaurant than in his den.

Before my move, the summer had been rough with my dad. When my last report card arrived, he'd even grounded me—or, in his Navy terms, put me on restriction. I'd graduated with honors and earned an ACT composite score in the ninety-ninth percentile, despite a low math score. I'd qualified as one of our school's five National Merit finalists and passed four college-level A.P. exams, with perfect scores in English and American History. However, I'd dozed through my last semester of trigonometry and failed it, and I'd flunked out of seminary, the daily Mormon religion class.

"Look," I'd said after a few days on restriction. "I'm starting the U in a couple months. I'm just gonna get an apartment now."

To my surprise, my dad had been in favor. "You need to start learning real life," he said. My mom, however, was upset. "If you don't want to live here, I feel like we've failed," she said. "At least stay your freshman year. You're not even eighteen yet."

"You haven't failed," I said to her. "I'm just ready now." But my reassurance didn't help. In the days before I moved out, she grew quiet and moody. Sometimes I saw her crying. I was the oldest of her nine children.

I met my dad at a burger place near the University of Utah. I felt glad the place was full of people smoking, so he wouldn't smell the cigarette smoke on me.

"You'll be eighteen in two months," he said after some small talk. "Have you asked your bishop about getting the Melchizedek priesthood?"

I already held the Aaronic priesthood, which I'd received at age twelve. After we saw *Star Wars* in 1977, my dad had compared the priesthood to the Force. All humans subconsciously remembered their premortal spiritual existence, so eternal concepts could pop up in anyone's story, even a non-Mormon like George Lucas. But all I'd ever done with the Aaronic priesthood was prepare, pass, and bless the sacrament on Sundays. I'd taken it seriously at first, but before long I was giggling during blessings and sneaking mouthfuls of sacramental bread.

"I don't think I'm ready for more priesthood." As I said the words, I felt a thrill, like the first time I jumped off a high dive.

My dad's eyebrows went up. He wiped his mouth. "Are you even attending church?"

"Not really, no."

The Sunday after I'd moved out, I'd gone back home and fulfilled my assignment to speak in sacrament meeting about faith or something. That had been my last time at church, and I didn't intend to go back. I cared so little about the church that I'd never bothered trying to believe or disbelieve it—I simply ignored it as white noise. If some kind of extraterrestrial "Lord" did somehow exist, I doubted he'd want his church to be so boring, with everyone thinking, acting, and looking the same. The church even described itself as a hive full of worker bees, as if that were a selling point.

In Dungeons & Dragons terms, the LDS church was lawful good and I was chaotic neutral, like the wizards and thieves I'd roleplayed in my younger teens. In D&D, neutral basically meant selfish—I did what I needed for my own comfort, but

I didn't hurt others for evil purposes, and I didn't conform to some one-size-fits-all system of good. Dark and light supernatural forces were just drama for movies, novels, and religions. God and the devil were just adult versions of Santa Claus and the Grinch. The universe undoubtedly held dimensions beyond the human senses, but science was the key to detecting such things.

Even if I'd believed the theology, Mormon culture was about as satisfying to me as cabbage water was to Charlie Bucket in the *Willy Wonka* movie. I felt no interest in the earthly Mormon path: Boy Scouts and basketball, then a two-year mission, followed by college, marriage, and decades of working to support a kid-infested household. The LDS church was a power-hungry corporation that controlled and manipulated people. At best, it was just a boring tradition for uptight, uncreative people.

My dad squinted at me, his jaw muscles working. In the past, he would've gotten upset about my *attitude*—growing up, that was the word I'd heard most, even more than *example*. "Who do you think you are?" he'd growl through gritted teeth. I could sort of understand what he meant—I knew I was emotionally lame in some ways, and I wasn't spiritual at all, if spirituality were even a real thing. Many aspects of human life seemed dumb to me, so I often felt aloof and sarcastic. If an attitude scale existed, I was probably only in the thirtieth percentile or lower. But I knew it was my personality, not something I could control—and neither could my dad. My recent journal entry was coming true:

> *My dad is imposing rules and restrictions upon me. He's particularly annoying in his efforts to make me more spiritual. Religion just doesn't interest me. I don't want him to take my refusal to embrace his values personally. I'm simply biding my time until I'm legally entitled to make my own decisions. I will eventually turn out the way I want, as even he admits.*

"I'm dreading telling your mom about this," my dad finally said. "Not that she wasn't already worried."

I looked into my lap. I hated the thought of making my mom cry, but I couldn't help being born Mormon and not liking it. My parents weren't my enemies, but I knew they'd been duped.

As we finished eating in silence, I decided not to mention that, in addition to dropping the church, I'd recently informed the Navy I no longer wanted my ROTC scholarship, the same scholarship my dad had won in high school. I just couldn't imagine myself in the military—I wasn't sure I even liked America, let alone wanted to defend it or help it dominate the world. My dad hadn't earned his Eagle Scout or served a Mormon mission, but he claimed the Navy had made him into a man. In Vietnam, he'd served as second-in-command of a minesweeper. More than a decade later, he still acted like a Navy officer, instead of letting us run free like the family of eleven kids across the street. He meant well, but why did he have to be so authoritative?

After the military, my parents had stayed in Southern California, where my dad went into banking. Two months before I turned eleven, they moved us to Utah in 1977. They built a new house in the Bountiful foothills near the geological bathtub ring left by an ancient inland sea, swapping our palm-accented view of Catalina Island for the primevally barren Great Salt Lake. Tired of L.A.'s traffic and property taxes, my dad was the one who'd wanted to move—my mom hadn't wanted to leave California, and I hadn't either. I wondered if I would've rebelled as much in California, where Mormonism didn't seem so boring and all-consuming.

Dropping me off at my apartment, my dad gave me a strained smile, a mix of friendliness, concern, and exasperation. "No matter what, you're always welcome back home."

I said thanks, but all I cared about was lighting my next cigarette.

When my great-aunt Sue called, I knew my dad had given her my number. She and Uncle Dick lived just a few blocks from my apartment. Their gothic, gray-stucco mansion stood surrounded by trees and ivy in Federal Heights, a neighborhood first established by the U.S. troops sent to wrangle the polygamous, theocratic Mormons.

Besides my dad's parents, Dick and Sue Bigelow were the people who'd most influenced him, he'd told us. They had seven kids, two younger than me. I admired the family's sophisticated mix of earthiness and worldliness, including their aloofness toward Mormonism. They were way more interesting than our Bigelow relatives down south in Utah County, who forbade candy and TV, slaughtered their own sheep, and homeschooled from the Book of Mormon and the U.S. Constitution. To me, the Utah County Bigelows seemed almost as fundamentalist as polygamists.

Aunt Sue was active in church, but Uncle Dick and their kids didn't seem to be, beyond Uncle Dick playing the pipe organ each Sunday for priesthood meeting. Camping once in a remote part of Utah's San Rafael Swell, I'd watched as Uncle Dick hiked nude except for boots, his swimsuit areas evenly tanned with the rest of his body, playing a recorder and dancing like a satyr among the red rocks. During my one sleepover at their mansion, I'd seen empty wine bottles in a dumbwaiter and a red can of Folgers coffee in the kitchen, and we'd tried smoking some Marlboros my hellion cousin stole from his dad. After swimming in their indoor pool, we took turns pulling down our suits, bending over, and spreading our cheeks for the other to look. Then we took the bus down to Trolley Square and snuck into two movies. Part of me envied this freewheeling life, but part of me felt relieved to go home.

Compared to our relatives, my parents were middle-range Mormons. They did some chaotic things like drink Coke, see

R-rated movies, and occasionally take us out for ice cream on Sundays, but they lawfully went to church each week, held family home evening on Monday nights, and attended the mysterious Salt Lake Temple downtown every month or two. Like a good Mormon homemaker, my mom bottled fruit and made clothes and bread. We'd tried growing vegetables, but after a few seasons we gave up, my dad acting as if we'd failed spiritually as much as practically.

Aunt Sue invited me over for breakfast on a Sunday morning. Walking through their posh, tree-lined neighborhood, I hoped I'd turn out like these Bigelows. I probably wouldn't be as wealthy, but I could be free-spirited and sophisticated. Religiously I was already becoming not only like Uncle Dick but also like his father, Percival, my great-grandfather who'd left the church. Percival was the son of a polygamist and his second of three wives.

As Aunt Sue led me into the dining room with its medievally massive table, I remembered how this house and family had always reminded me of the rich, bizarre Addams family on TV. My Uncle Dick looked and laughed a bit like the Addams father, Gomez, and he was similarly charming and cocksure in his weirdness. My cousin reminded me of the deviant Addams boy, Pugsley. Sitting at the table, I half-expected a tall, zombified butler to shamble in and rumble deeply, "You rang?" Instead, Aunt Sue brought me a plate of fancy eggs. I didn't see or hear any other family members.

I worried Aunt Sue might talk about religion, but instead we discussed college, books, and Salt Lake City itself. She was friends with Mayor Ted Wilson, and she was known citywide for her Addams family–ish Halloween costumes and decorations, as featured in the *Salt Lake Tribune*. As we chatted, occasionally she tried to draw out my opinions or plans, but I was a better listener than talker.

At one point, Aunt Sue screwed up her face and gave me a penetrating squint. Her eyes were dark and beady, and a red birthmark mottled part of her face.

"I'm just trying to figure out what's inside that head of yours," she said.

I wondered what was in there too, but I knew it definitely wasn't Mormonism. I wondered what life was like for Aunt Sue, believing in Mormonism with such a kooky-ooky family, in the words of the *Addams Family* theme song. I couldn't imagine Uncle Dick and my cousins as Mormon sheep. I hoped they never lost their coolness and individuality.

The next time I visited Bountiful, my mother seemed subdued, but she managed to smile at me. After Sunday dinner, the door-bell rang. I hoped it was just a neighbor or the home teachers from church, but someone said the door was for me. It was Brother Carter again. When I was younger, he'd taught my Sunday-school class, and now he was trying to save me from apostasy.

We sat on a living-room sofa. In the window behind us, a pollution-enhanced sunset glowed bloody over the Great Salt Lake. Two of my towheaded siblings peeked around a corner at us. Brother Carter balanced his briefcase on his knees. An engineer by profession, he wore a bushy moustache and frameless eyeglasses. He had on a tie, but his shirt was green instead of the usual Mormon white.

"Have you ever heard of *Sunstone?*" Brother Carter asked.

"Something to do with Nauvoo?"

"That's where the name comes from. The Nauvoo temple had big stones carved like the sun."

I'd seen an original sunstone statue in the restored 1840s Mormon village of Nauvoo, Illinois. Punkish-looking rays spiked out from the sun's head. The brow was furrowed, the sphinxlike eyes looked blank, and the lips pooched in a Mona Lisa smile. The statue was an artifact from Mormonism's early days of magic and chaos. For some reason, a sunstone was also on display at the Smithsonian in Washington D.C.

"What I want to show you is this." Brother Carter thumbed the briefcase clasps, letting out a double staccato. He lifted the lid and moved aside a pastel church manual. Underneath was a stack of *Sunstone* magazines.

As I watched him, I imagined how buzzy my next smoke would feel, after several hours without.

"You were in the gifted program at school, right?" Brother Carter asked.

"In California, yeah." After testing in the ninety-ninth percentile for IQ, I'd been designated a Mentally Gifted Minor and moved into a special class.

"I knew you were intelligent. This magazine is like Mormonism's gifted program."

He handed me an issue. The cover showed a human figure falling upside down, its body entwined by a black snake. One hand clutched an apple. The headline read, "Toward a Mormon Concept of Original Sin."

"Mormon culture doesn't have to be superficial and vanilla like this." Brother Carter gestured out a window. I glanced at the neighborhood's only non-Mormon house. A tall wrought-iron fence surrounded it, as if to repel missionaries and home teachers.

The word *vanilla* made me think of my weird recurring childhood dream. I'd stopped dreaming it when I entered puberty, but the dream had recently returned after I'd moved out. Wandering through a spacious white blankness, my dream self felt restless and bored. Occasionally I noticed a single white daisy growing, but I couldn't find anything else to hold my interest.

As I walked, I began hearing a faint pounding rhythm. The sound intrigued me. I wanted to find its source. Following the beat, I somehow walked below the whiteness, as if sinking underground. The pounding steadily grew faster and louder, giving me a queasy thrill. The lighting dimmed and turned orange. The air smelled greasy and mechanical. Ahead of me, something was doing something with amazing power, and I wanted to find out what. In the dream, I knew I had only two choices—the boring blank whiteness or this dark, energetic power.

Moving closer to the sound, I felt increasingly uneasy. I tried to calm myself by whistling a nonchalant tune, but I couldn't hear myself above the pounding. Soon I saw a large black machine, about the size of my family's van. It throbbed, banged, and blew out smoke. As I got closer, I saw pistons pumping up and down. I felt scared, but I still didn't want to return to the white blankness, which held nothing for me. I had to be brave and keep approaching the frantic machine. However, before I got close enough to understand what it was doing, I always woke up.

When Brother Carter finished talking, he left me some *Sunstone* issues. I glanced through a few. The articles had dry titles. "Obedience, Integrity, and the Paradox of Selfhood." "Excommunication: Metaphors of Discipline." "Eternity, Capacity, and the Will: Three Puzzles for a Mormon Aesthetics." "Genetic Self-Interest and Mormon Polygamy."

My mother came in, wiping her hands on a dishtowel. Her frosted hair was trimmed close. She wasn't fat, but her belly had never fully deflated after all her pregnancies. She was still wearing her homemade Sunday dress.

"What did Brother Carter say this time?" Her blue eyes looked red-rimmed and watery.

"He gave me these."

My mom sat down and picked up a magazine. The cover headline asked, "Are Children Almost Too Much to Bear?"

"Sometimes Brother Carter makes me tired."

"Don't worry. I'm not gonna read them."

She gave me a look. "Maybe they're better than nothing, in your case. So tell me, what *are* you going to do with your life?"

I didn't know how to answer such a question. If anything, I was waiting to see what my life would do with me. Just then, I heard the horn of Matt's old blue Pinto. Relief surged through me like a hormone.

"Wait just a second," my mom said. She hurried to the kitchen and came back with two Mason jars containing her home-bottled peaches. As she handed them to me, I saw hope in her eyes, as if her peaches could cure my spiritual disease. But I knew I probably wouldn't eat them. They were too sweet and pioneerish.

Speeding downhill, Matt and I cackled like robbers in a getaway car. The tips of our cigarettes glowed orange like the last traces of the sunset.

Chapter 3

"THERE'S STILL SOME SUMMER LEFT," MY ROOMMATE VIR-gil said late one night, after my friends had left. "Things will settle down when classes start. Yes?"

"Sure."

Our shabby, orange-carpeted studio was on the top floor of an old yellow house on Wolcott Street, just yards away from the University of Utah campus. Several sorority and fraternity houses stood nearby, including the ones where my parents had first met in the early 1960s. Virgil and I each paid one hundred dollars a month for rent, phone, and daily delivery of the *Salt Lake Tribune*.

My roommate was a prematurely balding future lawyer who'd graduated from Salt Lake's East High School, where my mom also went. I knew Virgil from debate meets—during my preppie phase, I'd joined Bountiful High's debate team as an extemporaneous speaker. He liked driving me around Salt Lake to visit his favorite neighborhoods, restaurants, and bookshops. He did nearly all the talking, but occasionally I'd make a dry quip, and he'd let a moment pass and then break into laughing. On Sundays, Virgil sometimes invited me to church, but I made excuses.

Virgil didn't have friends over, but my friends showed up every day, commandeering my stereo and replacing Virgil's Bach and Beethoven with punk and new wave. Virgil also had some old Beatles records, and we all liked those. Around my friends, Virgil acted like an anthropologist fascinated by our styles and behaviors, while my friends found him amusingly egg-headed and old-mannish.

Whenever Virgil was home, my friends and I smoked on the Cabbage Patch's rickety back landing or out front on the porch roof, where we could watch the sun set beyond downtown Salt Lake's red-blinking towers. When Virgil was away, we smoked inside, stinking up his clothes and everything else. The first time I dared smoke in front of Virgil, he snatched the cigarette and surprised me by bringing it to his lips. I said a silent prayer that he would smoke it, but he pantomimed someone trying to be sophisticated and then threw down the cigarette hard enough to explode its cherry on the pavement.

Soon after I moved out, I started working downtown at Honey Bear Toys in the Crossroads mall. About every hour, a mother phoned to ask if we had any Cabbage Patch Kids in stock. One day, a shipment of the ugly dolls arrived. That evening, I described the near-riot to my friends. Janet told us the myth of how a boy named Xavier first discovered the Cabbage Patch Kids by following a bunny-bee behind a waterfall into a magical cabbage patch. The bunny-bees used their rabbit ears as wings so they could pollinate the cabbages with magic crystals that grew into babies.

From then on, we called my apartment the Cabbage Patch.

Matt often brought Tina to the Cabbage Patch. Her shtick was girlish airheadedness, but I could tell she was bright in her own effervescent way. She was always telling hilarious stories about weird people she'd met. If Tina and I had gone to high school together, I would've stared at her nonstop. "I can tell you like me," I would've fantasized her saying to me. "I like you too, so let's get together." Then she'd train me how to be her boyfriend.

Maybe she'd even make me a detailed schedule, like my mother had done when I was little, assigning me a mix of jobs and play. I wondered if Tina knew Matt was bisexual.

Sometimes Lisa brought stray punks to the Cabbage Patch. Most intriguing was Maeve, a punker who wore a butch black-leather jacket but also pointy-toed, cream-colored pumps. Buzzed up the back, her black-dyed hair hung low in front. Like my Aunt Sue, Maeve had a birthmark under one eye, as if she'd cried red wine. She had an authentic British accent, and I loved her mocking, ultracool, no-B.S. punk attitude. Lisa claimed Maeve's dad had been an original '70s punk rocker in London. While Tina's eyes sparkled, Maeve's glinted. I fantasized about the two girls competing for me, little dreaming it would actually happen.

Maeve occasionally rolled up her leather jacket as a pillow and slept on the floor. Meanwhile, Janet insinuated herself into the Cabbage Patch full-time. During the day, she lounged in a T-shirt and panties, using her long fingernails to pluck flakes of tuna from a can. Occasionally she shoplifted M&Ms and warmed them with a blow dryer before eating them. I saw too much of Janet's pale, chunky body. Her underpants couldn't contain her massive bush, and I wished she could transfer some of her bra load to Tina.

One night, we threw a party at the Cabbage Patch. Lisa hollowed out a watermelon and made jungle juice with a key ingredient called Everclear. It was easy to drink—too easy. Some Bountiful high schoolers crashed the party, including my younger brother. The next day, I could only recall the party's first hour or so. I'd always thought alcohol blackout meant unconsciousness, but I realized the drunken me could say and do things I'd never say or do while sober, and I wouldn't remember it. I felt vaguely worried I might've said rude things to the Bountiful kids, especially to one pretty blonde. When I pressed Lisa and Matt for details, they cringed.

"Just leave it be." Lisa rubbed my shoulders. "Just leave it be."

I remembered something I'd heard an itinerant Mormon preacher say. The word *preacher* wasn't used in Mormonism, but it suited Lynn Bryson. He dressed more like a radio DJ than an LDS speaker, with a dark, pearl-buttoned shirt and longish hair blow-dried straight back like Wolfman Jack's. Traveling around Mormon America in his motorhome, Bryson had reached our Bountiful ward in 1980. The bishop called an emergency meeting so Bryson could warn us about the satanic conspiracy in rock music and Dungeons & Dragons.

According to Lynn Bryson, the Latin for "alcohol" was *spiritus*, which also meant "soul." People drank alcohol because, deep down, they wanted to escape the mundane and glimpse God's higher reality. But alcohol was actually just the devil's spiritual counterfeit. "Intoxication weakens your defenses against evil spirits," Brother Bryson had preached. "If you give them any opening, these spirits will start taking you over."

I didn't believe in evil spirits. But it was strange to imagine myself acting like a different person, like Dr. Jekyll and Mr. Hyde. Did alcohol somehow allow the subconscious to take over?

KCGL had grown popular enough to sponsor bigger concerts. At the Violent Femmes show, I spotted one of my Kimball cousins and made sure he saw me smoking. The summer's biggest event was two British new-wave bands under the stars at Park-West. Eurythmics projected some cool decadence, but Howard Jones was almost Mormonishly positive and wholesome, which made me dislike him.

The night before the concert, Lisa rented a Park City condo. Among the alcohol was a bottle of wine Chad claimed was over a hundred years old, which he'd stolen from his dad. It didn't take me long to drink myself into blackout again.

Suddenly I snapped back into full consciousness. I was out-side in the moonlight, stumbling down a sidewalk. The night air felt cool. Someone was pulling me along by the fly of my jeans.

It was Tina.

"What're we doing?" I asked. I had no idea what time it was or which condo building was ours. My groin tingled.

Giggling, Tina led me to Matt's sky-blue Pinto. Finding the doors unlocked, we climbed into the backseat.

"What are we doing?" I asked again. I felt buzzed but alert. Earlier Matt had whispered that Tina liked me and he didn't mind if we got together, because it was about time I got a girl-friend. I'd wondered if he were setting me up for some kind of prank.

Tina smiled at me. "I could tell you wanted to come out here with me."

We began making out. Despite my lack of experience, my body knew what to do. I didn't feel any Mormon guilt or inhibi-tion. When most of our clothes were off, Tina stopped me. "I don't know you enough yet," she said in a giggly voice.

"That's OK." I glanced out the window, half-expecting Matt and Chad to drag me naked from the car.

I tried to reengage with Tina, but she stopped me again. "Tell you what," she said. "We can do it on one condition."

"What?"

"I move into the Cabbage Patch."

"Seriously?" I felt a flush of excitement.

Tina told me how much she hated her Mormon parents. She had a job at Crown Burger, so she could help pay rent. "I could do my senior year at East High," she said. "It would be so fun!"

Tina didn't follow my usual crush preference of brown hair and brown eyes, but that was OK. Living together, we'd be like a married couple but without any wedding crap and with all our friends still hanging out with us.

"It's a deal," I said. I felt a pang about Virgil, but I figured he could just move back home. I was the one who'd found the studio, after all.

I tried to angle myself into position, but Tina laughed and pushed me away. "Not in Matt's car, silly. At the Cabbage Patch, as soon as I get my stuff moved in."

As the sun rose, Tina and I walked down to the bus stop. I still felt tipsy, but I'd promised my dad I'd get to Bountiful by 8:00 a.m. My parents were out of town, and my dad's secretary needed the morning off from answering his phone. His office was in the basement of our house.

Tina wanted to come with me. As we rode the bus down Parley's Canyon, the sun shone too brightly from behind us. Tina kept smiling at an old man, focusing her girlish energy on him until he sat up straighter and smiled back. Sometimes Tina's playful, sensual, droopy-eyed expressions reminded me of Marilyn Monroe.

At the house, we met my dad's secretary in the front hall. She'd stayed overnight with my eight younger siblings. Sometimes she seemed like our aunt or something. Occasionally when I'd gotten home from school, I'd found her napping like Goldilocks in my basement bedroom. As we chatted, I wondered if the secretary could smell the smoke and alcohol on us. Glancing down at Tina's short-shorts, she gave me a worried look. Then her face crumpled even more, and I knew she'd spotted my new earring.

A few nights earlier, while we were drinking beer, Chad had said, "Hey, let's turn Biggs more punk." He numbed my earlobe with ice and pierced my ear with Matt's old starter stud. I'd made sure it was my left ear, because the right ear meant gay. The earring made me feel like I'd been claimed, somehow.

In the basement, I fell asleep on my dad's La-Z-Boy while Tina went back upstairs to play with my siblings. The business phone rang only a couple of times. That afternoon, I took the car my parents had left home and drove Tina to her parents' house. On our way, she described what a redneck place Kearns was, and I tried to outdo her with how Mormon Bountiful was.

At Tina's, I waited in the car while she got her stuff. With my window down, I thought I could hear shouting from inside the house. Soon she came out with a backpack and suitcase, and she slammed the front door. As we pulled away, I saw a curtain move in the front window. Tina took several minutes to calm down.

When we reached the Cabbage Patch, no one was there. The studio smelled awful, a mix of smoke, tuna, unwashed clothes, unvacuumed carpet, and the house's oldness. Tina got busy cramming her bright-colored clothes into my dresser and closet, occasionally flashing me an encouraging smile. Then she pulled down the queen-size Murphy bed from the wall.

"That's Virgil's bed," I said. My small childhood bed sat in a corner, next to my dresser covered with the Wacky Package stickers I'd adored as a kid, mocking consumer products—Crest toothpaste was Crust, Ritz crackers were Ratz, Listerine mouthwash was Blisterine. I still found it surreal to see this furniture in this setting.

"He won't know." Tina smiled at me, her eyes crinkling almost shut. As we undressed, she didn't say anything about a condom. Her total engulfment thrilled me like nothing before—but, of course, it was over too fast.

Later, I drove us back up to Park City. I kept thinking how freaky it was that sex could happen so easily. I felt surprised it didn't happen more often and more openly. Everyone was just walking around with their genitals under two thin fabric layers. My passiveness had made me miss out on so much.

I remembered the church's teaching that fornication would make me feel terrible. Even after scrubbing myself raw in the shower, I'd still feel dirty. But so far, I just felt a little empty, like the time I'd peeked early at my Christmas presents. I didn't feel dirty or guilty, and I wanted to do it again. I considered Tina and myself essentially married now.

When we met our friends at ParkWest, the boys all clapped me on the back, correctly assuming I'd lost my virginity. I wondered if Matt had slept with Tina. If so, how many times and how recently? I decided I didn't want to know. As daylight waned, we claimed a spot high on the grassy mountainside. The previous winter, I'd skied down frozen white powder several feet directly above this grass. At first Tina sat by me, taking her turns nipping from Chad's flask. But then she spotted some people she knew. They looked gothically vampirish like the Cure, with black and white clothes, red lips, white faces, teased black hair, and heavy eyeliner.

"See you later!" Tina gave me a cringing, pitying smile and ran off.

I felt like she'd punched me in the stomach. Weren't we a couple now, and shouldn't we always stay together?

My first few weeks with Tina went OK, except we rarely got any privacy. I didn't feel Mormon guilt, but it wasn't how I'd imagined my first relationship. Just a few weeks before moving out, I'd written in my journal: *It's best just to be friends with girls, not force romance. When you get involved with someone, friendship goes down in exchange for passion. I'm lucky I haven't gotten involved yet. I've saved a lot of heartache, hassle, and enemies. When the right friend comes along and a romance develops over time, that will be nice.*

When Tina wasn't working, she mostly hung out at the Cabbage Patch, only occasionally going out with other friends, which I tried not to let upset me. Matt, Lisa, Chad, and Vince kept coming over almost daily, but Maeve showed up less often. And when she did, she always gave me a glinty incredulous look. *How can you take that whorish teenybopper seriously?* Even in my mind, Maeve's voice had a smoker-raspy British accent. Sometimes I got the feeling she wanted to beat Tina up.

One of the few times we had the Cabbage Patch to ourselves, I took time to explore Tina. I figured females must have some kind of interior knob that males were supposed to diddle. Eventually I came across something deep inside Tina that seemed right. It felt slick and rubbery, dimpled in the middle like a Hostess mini-donut. When I went to work on it, however, Tina put her hand on mine.

"What are you doing?" she asked.

"I guess I don't know."

She giggled. Then she showed me where to press and how to flutter my hand in a certain way, not unlike a violinist. *Jeez, no wonder I missed it,* I thought.

When other people were around, we tried to find places for quickies. Once, we lay down together on the bathroom floor, but it was too hard and filthy. Another time, we tried in the short hallway between the main room and kitchen. The hallway had doors on both sides, but it was too cramped, and people kept trying to come through. While smoking out on the porch roof one evening, we realized the next-door window opened into an unoccupied bedroom. Scooting aside paint cans and trays, we stretched out on the plastic tarp covering the carpet, enjoying the relative luxury. We visited the bedroom several more times until it was rented out.

Instead of getting mad about all this activity, Virgil started fading away. Increasingly often, he slept at his parents' house, and his stuff had begun disappearing from the Cabbage Patch. Sometimes he gave me a confused, disappointed look. Inwardly I shrugged. It wasn't like I'd planned what would fill the vacuum once I got rid of Mormonism.

Janet had taken over my twin-size bed, so on the final night Virgil slept in his Murphy bed, Tina and I made a nest of blankets on the floor. In the middle of the night, she climbed astride me. The floor made no noise, so we let ourselves go. Suddenly I realized Virgil was sitting up in his Murphy bed, silhouetted against the moonlit window. I rolled Tina off, and we pulled a blanket over our heads and tried not to giggle. Janet later admitted she'd watched us too, wanting to learn how to be on top. I supposed I couldn't blame Virgil for not sleeping there again.

Living with two girls, I felt like Jack Tripper in *Three's Company.* My mom didn't like that TV show, but I'd watched it whenever I could. Unlike Jack, I didn't have to pretend I was gay so the landlord would let me live with two females. Sometimes I tried to imagine the two girls agreeing to share me. It sounded coolly chaotic neutral, but I couldn't realistically see myself with two partners at once. How had my great-great-great-grandfather Heber C. Kimball kept up with seventeen childbearing wives? It sounded exhausting, not fun. I couldn't imagine how Mormonism had ever allowed it. My family felt proud we were from Heber's real wife, the first one, whose name was Vilate.

On warm summer nights when neighboring frats held keggers, we strolled from house to house. Tina could usually get us into frat parties for free. The boys ogled her and sneered at me, making me feel like an imposter, not man enough to have such a girlfriend. Eighty percent of frat boys were better looking than me, and ninety-eight percent could've beaten me at any sport. I wished I knew how to project to other males that I owned Tina. Before long, my fear of frat boys would be justified.

Chapter 4

MATT HAD BEEN SMOKING CIGARETTES FOR YEARS, but he refused to try pot. "Dude, it's not even as strong as alcohol," Chad told him. But Matt wouldn't take a single toke. I was nervous about pot too, but Matt's refusal made me more willing. I didn't have many opportunities to be cooler than him.

The first time I smoked pot, Chad told me I probably wouldn't get high. We sat on mismatched chairs around the Cabbage Patch's wobbly kitchen table. Using a contraption from Cosmic Aeroplane's basement headshop, Lisa made a joint for each of us, enjoying the process as much as a kid using a Play-Doh machine. However, her joints came out too skinny and tight, hard to draw air through. Sure enough, I didn't feel much highness.

I'd wanted to try pot ever since I was about six. In Torrance, California, a neighbor girl had told me her older brother smoked grass from their backyard. I checked our backyard to see if we had any special-looking grass. I knew Mormons couldn't smoke cigarettes, which I secretly thought smelled good, but I'd never heard a rule against smoking grass. Plucking random blades, I clamped them between my lips, but they wouldn't smoke.

At white-trashy Bountiful Junior High in 1979, a new kid arrived from Kentucky. He seemed normal at first, with his terrycloth polo shirts with big collars and his hair parted in the middle with feathered sides. But soon he started wearing Black

Sabbath and Iron Maiden shirts, and his hair grew long and greasy. Sometimes his eyes looked puffy and bloodshot, and he smelled like burning leaves. I envied him for getting taken by the stoners. Sometimes I wished I'd been born to lousy parents.

In my earlier teens, I'd spent hours listening to Rush albums while reading fantasy trilogies. The song "A Passage to Bangkok" described visiting the world's best pot-growing locations. If guys as smart as Rush could smoke weed and make such creative music, maybe marijuana could make me more creative too. As Black Sabbath sang in "Sweet Leaf," maybe pot could introduce me to hidden parts of my own brain.

No one invited me to try pot until high school, and then it was two guys in my LDS ward. "Biggs, you'd be so hilarious high," one said. The three of us had received our Eagle Scout awards together, and on Sundays we blessed the sacrament bread and water. I wondered where their pot came from. While Bountiful Junior had seemed mostly cruddy, preppies dominated Bountiful High and any stoners laid low. I said no because I didn't want to upset my parents, but I sensed my time was approaching.

The second time I smoked pot, I was in the backseat of Lisa's car. Chad pushed me to take hit after hit from a small wooden pipe, making me hold in the ganja smoke as long as I could. When we reached the parking lot of the Maxim, a new-wave club in the middle of the Salt Lake Valley, Chad sat me down on the front bumper and chopped his hands back and forth in my peripheral vision until I was speeding down a narrow channel, like Luke Skywalker flying his X-wing inside a Death Star trench. When Chad suddenly smacked me on the forehead, my brain exploded. Groaning with pleasure, I eased myself back onto the warm hood.

What I liked most about pot was the giggling. Stoned, sometimes I'd be chatting with someone and realize we'd both been talking about totally different things. I'd try to explain, and they wouldn't understand what I meant, and we'd both fall into laughing seizures. Giggling high in public places, I felt a little paranoid, but it was fun, like acting scared in a haunted house I knew wasn't real. I loved how pot made music multicolored and three-dimensional. However, I found the cottonmouth and the munchies bothersome. Sometimes my stoned thoughts reminded me of the mental gobbledygook that came right before sleep.

For the rest of the summer, Chad and Lisa made sure I smoked dope every day. People liked getting high with me not only because I had the Cabbage Patch but also because I spouted bizarre thoughts and messed with their heads. Unlike alcohol, marijuana never blacked me out or hung me over. I felt almost angry Mormonism had kept me from getting high. Instead, they'd tried to talk me into something warm and fuzzy called "the gift of the Holy Ghost," but I'd never once felt it.

I'd started collecting punk flyers from walls and poles around downtown and the U. Salt Lake punk bands had names like Massacre Guys, The Stench, Bad Yodelers, Victims Willing, Potato Heads, and Maimed for Life. I loved the flyers' subversive, irreverent graphics mocking politics, religion, corporations, and consumers. Punk flyers were like a rawer, darker form of *Mad* magazine, which I'd idolized as a younger teen.

On a warm summer night, Matt, Lisa, Vince, and I cruised down State Street in Lisa's tan, sun-blotched Honda hatchback. Lisa turned right on Thirteenth South into a rougher part of Salt Lake and pulled into the parking lot of a rundown brick building. Foot-high black letters spelled out INDIAN CENTER.

"Is this the punk jig?" I asked, feeling excited but nervous.

"Gig, not jig," Matt said. Lisa let out a snort.

After Lisa cut the engine, we stayed in our seats, staring out the windows. "Even the cars are punk," Matt said. Some were spray-painted with the anarchy symbol or band logos. I recognized the stylized DK of the Dead Kennedys and Black Flag's four black dominoes. Between cars, we saw punkers dragging on cigarettes and taking swigs from paper-bagged bottles. One girl's fuchsia mohawk rose high like the sail of a Chinese junk.

Vince took off on his own, and I followed Lisa and Matt up the crumbling concrete steps. Taped to the door was a neon-green flyer listing four bands: B.G.K. from Amsterdam, Cause for Alarm from New York City, Adrenalin O.D. from New Jersey, and Septic Death from Boise, Idaho. I recognized the horror-comic logo of Raunch Records, which I'd heard was located under a freeway viaduct in an industrial slum wandered by homeless drug addicts.

As we passed through the lobby, I saw a stoic-faced Native American standing against a wall. He wore a salt-and-pepper ponytail and a blue windbreaker zipped to his neck, as if for protection. The local Indians must've been desperate, renting their community hall to Salt Lake's punk tribe. Reaching the ticket taker, I felt like I was walking into a Halloween party without a costume. My only slightly punk element was the stud in my ear. As Lisa paid for us, I untucked my homemade green-checkered shirt and tried roughing up my side-parted, yellow-white hair, but the thatch sprang back into place like always.

We'd arrived between bands, so the lights were on. Even with the windows open, the hall was hazy with smoke, as if fireworks had just gone off. The milling punks were as varied as creatures on a coral reef. Some had buzzed or shaved heads, with plain jeans and T-shirts, wallet chains, and combat boots. Others looked more elaborate like British punks, with spiked and colored hair, outlandish thrift-store clothes, studded bracelets and dog collars, and leather or denim vests or jackets, some painted with pseudo-military logos and slogans.

I spotted my Pugsley Addams cousin, feeling no surprise to learn he was a Salt Lake punk. His head was buzzed, and he wore a torn T-shirt, black schoolboy shorts, and old leather military boots. Sneering, he looked me up and down and then turned away. I didn't blame him for dissing me—I still looked so preppy and Mormon. But I remembered how, not so long ago, he'd loved mainstream rock bands like Styx.

Lisa waved over a girl with choppy blue-black hair, heavy black makeup, and skimpy, torn black clothes and fishnet. Her face was pale, with prominent cheeks and a cleft chin.

"Huh." The girl looked me up and down. "I never expected to see *you* here."

"He's ours now." Matt grabbed my shoulder. "We stole him from the Mormons."

I realized the girl was Holly, one of my Bountiful High classmates. Last I remembered, Holly had been a normal Mormon teenybopper, but then she'd disappeared from school. I'd heard she was suspended for showing up wearing a mohawk, a shredded jacket held together by safety pins, and rusty nails poking out of her combat boots. Then I heard she'd been institutionalized for doing something obscene with blue plastic Smurf toys.

As we watched Holly move away, Lisa whispered, "I think she's shooting heroin."

The moment Cause for Alarm started playing, punks spazzed out as if electrocuted. Thrashing and skanking in a circle, they lifted their knees, pumped their elbows, and slammed against each other. At first, I hung back with other intimidated new wavers and just watched. But the hard, fast, angry music drew me closer to the mosh pit. I felt waves of body heat and caught whiffs of yeasty sweat. I watched for a spiked yellow mohawk that kept coming around like a yellow shirt in a laundromat dryer.

Part of me wanted to join the ruckus, until I saw a thin, pimply, preppy-looking kid fall down. I thought he'd be trampled, but a muscly skinhead wearing red boots and suspenders pulled him up and shoved him out of the pit. Then I saw two punks lock together in a combat-hug, hitting and clawing each other's backs. They burst out of the pit like a spark from a bonfire, and other punks pulled them apart and walked them away in opposite directions.

When a she-punk climbed onstage, I realized it was Maeve. She was wearing her black leather jacket over a white T.S.O.L. shirt, with a chrome-studded leather belt sitting crooked on her hips. She spat at a guitarist's feet and bumped against him, but the music was too fast and distorted to tell if he missed any notes. Stepping to the edge of the stage, Maeve lifted her arms to the crucifix, lolled her bangs to one side, and let herself fall.

I thought she was a goner, but punks raised their hands and held her high. They moved her along until she landed on her scuffed, ultra-fem pumps. Instead of moving away from the male mosh pit, she dove back in. Her knees and elbows pumped. Her bangs whipped up and down. Her protective jacket absorbed body blows. The more she thrashed, the bigger she sneered. She was the smallest, feistiest punk.

Punk was so wild, creative, and underground that I almost couldn't believe it was happening. Surely nothing this cool had ever emerged before on planet Earth. I felt like I'd finally arrived at the monster rumpus in *Where the Wild Things Are*. What mastermind had thought up this scene? I couldn't detect any adult or corporate involvement. I wondered how punk I could get. Like ipecac syrup, maybe punk would purge my system of all the white, goopy, flavorless Mormonism I'd ingested since birth.

I needed to undo my preppiness. The next time I went home to Bountiful, I took along an extra pair of jeans. After dinner, I locked myself in my old basement bathroom with a knife and a jug of bleach. Sitting on the edge of the tub, I stabbed random holes in the pants, trying to feel outraged about America's shallow, oppressive society and Mormonism's bland, controlling, one-size-fits-all conformity. I knew I was forcing it, but I didn't want to wait for my punkness to naturally emerge. I didn't know if I even had any innate punkness.

As I worked, I couldn't help thinking of the Charles Manson killers. In Long Beach, California, at the very moment in 1969 when my mom learned about the Manson murders on TV, I was sitting in her lap as a toddler, and her fear infused me. As I grew up, my Manson fear morphed into fascination. The book *Helter Skelter* came out when I was seven. In stores and libraries, I gulped down as much of it as possible when my mom wasn't looking. The murders made me queasy, but I loved learning about the Manson family and their hippie attitudes and drugs, especially LSD.

When the pants seemed perforated enough, I laid them out in the bathtub and dribbled bleach on them. I was going for anarchy, but the results looked contrived. It reminded me of my earlier struggles with pants. During elementary school, I'd usually worn corduroy pants. When I started school in Utah, a fellow sixth-grader came up to me and said, "You're not wearing the right pants." He wasn't being mean—he knew I'd just moved to Utah, and he was trying to help. The kid's denim H.A.S.H. jeans flared wide enough to cover his shoes, with gold stitching decorating both legs. On the back pocket was a large star like the symbol of Kiss guitarist Paul Stanley. I asked my parents for a pair of H.A.S.H. jeans, but they said no.

School shopping for seventh grade, I'd found a pair of dark-brown corduroys that flared over my shoes. The pants were too long, so my mom cut off the bottom three inches and sewed a new hem. I wore the pants often enough that by springtime they'd faded to light brown. When the pants got too short, my mom hemmed back on the dark-brown bottom pieces. I got mocked so much that I stopped wearing them.

Pants aside, what really needed punking was my hair. Before my teens, my hair had been blindingly white, which made me feel special, like the blondish, psychic kids in *Escape from Witch Mountain*. Now my hair was more yellow-blond, and it felt like an outgrowth of my milquetoast personality. Whenever I saw other light-haired males, I thought they looked less masculine. In *The Outsiders*, a novel I'd adored in seventh grade, Ponyboy had disguised himself by bleaching his hair to my color, and his fellow greasers had said it was lame.

Around that time, I'd tried parting my hair in the middle like the cool guys did. My dad cut my hair—"A trick I learned in the Navy," he often half-joked—but he didn't know how to feather it. I tried controlling my hair with a long-handled Goody comb, which I always carried in my back pocket. But even when I used water, my hair was too thick to stay, and my cowlicks made the two sides look lopsided.

When I was sixteen, the Mormon church featured me on the cover of a missionary pamphlet titled *After Baptism, What?* Dressed all in white, I'd stood in a swimming pool with a pre-ternaturally white-haired, eight-year-old girl, holding my arm to the square as if about to baptize her. On the printed brochure, our heads glowed with pure, otherworldly light. Eventually the church replaced us with a more realistic Hispanic father and son.

Now I wanted to violate all that Mormon hair on my head. But dyeing it, shaving it, or even just buzzing it felt too outrageous—I still wanted to be able to look normal when I needed. Back home in the Cabbage Patch, I pulled on my new punk pants and spiked my hair like the bleach-headed Billy Idol.

"Why're you such a wannabe?" Tina asked, scowling. She thought punk was dumb.

I wanted to attend punk gigs more often, but my friends preferred the Maxim. We never attended the club's country or gay nights, but on new-wave nights we'd mousse up our hair and dress like British bands. Using one of Janet's makeup pencils, Matt showed me how to blacken my lower eyelid rims so I'd look more decadent in the dark. At a thrift store, I found some skanky black shoes with pointy toes, probably originally worn by some 1960s businessman.

Whenever we first entered the Maxim, Matt would scan the crowd. "Lots of vibes here tonight," he'd murmur. His eyes would lock onto a potential hookup, usually a girl but sometimes a boy. Vibes intrigued me, but I found them confusing and embarrassing. The Cabbage Patchers mostly just danced as a group.

Lisa tried to dress new wave, but she looked more like a 1950s greaser. Sometimes she rolled a pack of cigarettes into her T-shirt sleeve or tucked a cigarette behind her ear. She walked around the Maxim offering snuff to people. I tried the powdered tobacco, but I was already nicotine buzzed, so it only tickled my nose. Sometimes Lisa took out a little tin of tingly Tiger Balm and rubbed it onto people's lips.

Whenever the DJ played "What I Like about You" by the Romantics, Lisa and I formed our own two-person mosh pit. Skanking and pogoing, we ricocheted off each other, cushioned by Lisa's nonsexual hips, breasts, and butt. Her hair flew out frizzy everywhere. She whooped and laughed. Sometimes people formed a circle around us to watch.

A few punkers came to the Maxim. Among new wavers, punks usually wore their hair droopy, but sometimes I saw an erect mohawk moving through the dancers like a shark fin. To me, punk and new wave were yin-yang. Punk made girls more boyish, while new wave made boys more girlish. Boy punkers scammed on girl new wavers, who tried to keep them from fighting, going to jail, or OD'ing. While effeminate new-wave boys were common, girl punkers like Maeve were rare.

I felt more drawn to punk, which seemed like a deeper, darker, cooler level of the underground. New wave required less effort and risk, but I knew I couldn't maximize my personal coolness until I went fully punk, even if I wasn't fully sure yet what that meant.

Chapter 5

WE DREADED THE END OF THE CABBAGE PATCH SUM-
mer. Matt and I would soon begin university classes.
Chad and Tina would start their senior years of high school.
Janet might finally get a job down at the mall. Lisa would keep
doing data entry. Our punkest friends, Maeve and Vince, didn't
seem to have any plans.

When a cocaine dealer moved in downstairs, things with Tina
began falling apart. From our window, I watched her greet the
guy and help him carry in his boxes. His hair was long, and he
wore a cowboy hat decorated with peacocky feathers. Over the
next few days, Tina spent increasing amounts of time downstairs,
and I felt increasingly jealous. As if in reaction to cocaine, she
began grinding her teeth in her sleep. I wondered how she was
paying for it.

"You've got to meet him," Tina said. "He's so cool!"

One evening, she took me downstairs through a door in a
corner of our studio. Until the dealer moved in, this door had
always been locked from the other side. After only a minute of
small talk, the guy offered me free cocaine. But I was too scared
to try it, assuming I'd get instantly hooked and soon end up
in jail.

In high school, I'd enjoyed poring over the drug chart in our
health textbook. Alcohol, nicotine, and pot were givens—I'd

known I'd eventually try those, when the time was right. I hadn't felt attracted to harder, addictive drugs like cocaine and heroin, especially if they involved a needle. However, I'd felt a strong desire to experiment with psychedelics. PCP sounded too crazy, but I hoped someone would someday offer me LSD, which sounded almost magical.

I watched as Tina snorted the powder lines I'd refused. As the drug kicked in, she gazed at the dealer with adoring gratitude. I felt queasy.

Without definite evidence, I kept trying to trust Tina. However, sometimes I wondered if I were getting the cocaine dealer's sloppy seconds. One evening, I arrived home to find Tina sitting on my childhood bed with a frat boy, making out.

"What the hell?" I cried.

The frat boy jumped up and brushed past me without making eye contact. I caught a whiff of his Polo, the trendy cologne that came in a green bottle.

"It didn't mean anything." Tina tried to hug me, but I moved away. "I didn't want to be rude to him."

"Maybe you should just move out."

Over the next few days, Tina tried to make me feel bad for her. She claimed an older cousin had molested her countless times. Also, she was bulimic. I knew about anorexia because of the skinny singer Karen Carpenter, but I didn't know the word *bulimia*. Tina explained she couldn't stop herself from binging on food and then throwing it up.

Suddenly I understood the multicolored splashes I'd seen around our toilet bowl. "So, when I got you dinner at Rio Grande Café and you went to the restroom, you threw it all up?"

"Probably." Tina gave me a cringing smile. "I don't remember."

She lifted her top lip to show me the brown stains on her teeth, which I'd already noticed. "That's from stomach acid," she said.

Growing up in Boise, Idaho, Tina had been chunky. In junior high, she decided getting thin would solve her problems. However, she didn't have the discipline for anorexia. Friends introduced her to diet pills, but they made her shaky and moody. She learned how to gag herself after eating, using a toothbrush handle to avoid bite marks on her hand. For her first laxative overdose, she took thirty pills and lost twenty pounds overnight. However, she got so dehydrated that her stomach, legs, and arms cramped up. When she drank coffee, it went straight through her, trickling out her bottom still hot.

Next time, Tina took fifty laxatives. Her dad found her curled up on the bathroom floor. At the hospital, the nurses struggled to get IVs flowing in her shriveled veins. As soon as they left, Tina turned off the machine so she wouldn't fatten back up. The doctors said she'd nearly suffered a heart attack because her heart lining was so dried out. After three days in the hospital, Tina was transferred to the psych ward for anorexia treatment. She let them catch her doing anorexic things like hiding food in her clothes. The staff didn't realize she was throwing up most of what she ate.

Back home, a bulimic friend taught Tina how to vomit simply by bending over and squeezing her side. Drinking water and carbonated soda made throwing up easier. The best binge was raw cake batter because it tasted good coming back up. Greasy donuts were hardest to puke. In one sitting, the two could consume a whole box of Cheerios and gallon of milk or a whole loaf of bread and jar of peanut butter. Their bellies would bloat like pregnancy. They competed to see who could swallow the most, binging until food started blocking their breathing. Then they'd watch each other barf.

After more laxative overdoses, Tina ended up in the state mental hospital. Her roommate had multiple personality disorder and constantly imitated others. During a drug search, the staff found four baggies of vomit under the girl's bed. Imitating Tina, she'd stolen baggies from the kitchen. Tina always threw her barf bags out the window.

Tina's parents finally convinced authorities that her laxative overdoses always came right before menstruation, which proved she had PMS. Although originally committed for at least a year, Tina was released after only three months, as long as she agreed to participate in a PMS support group. But then her dad's employer had transferred him to Salt Lake.

"Now I'm way more careful," Tina said, giggling.

"You look perfect to me," I said. "You can stop it now." After everything Tina had been through, I wondered how she stayed so fresh and bubbly. Whenever I tickled her back, I could feel soft plumpness under her skin.

"Crown Burger isn't the best place for me to work." Tina gave me a sheepish frown. "Unlimited fries and strawberry shakes! Now you know why I take Tagamet. And why I don't like smoking weed—the munchies wig me out. But I love cigarettes and coke. They help me lose weight!"

When Matt heard Tina could throw up just by pinching her side, he wanted to learn how. "I could eat as much I want!" he said. Tina took him into the bathroom. We could hear him retching, but he couldn't vomit even with a toothbrush gag.

The next time Tina's anorexic friend Daphne came over, Tina wasn't home, but Daphne still wanted to come inside. With her big blue eyes and frizzy bleached hair, Daphne seemed innocent and fragile, her head dollishly too large for her bony body. When she spoke in her earnest Utah Mormon accent, I heard insecurity in her voice.

"I gotta tell you, Tina's the most Christlike person I know," Daphne said, watching me drag on my cigarette. "She's helped me so much—I could never tell you how much. She's visited me in the hospital prolly twenty times."

Daphne told me how Tina once took the weirdest kid at Kearns High School to the prom, a chubby, spacey person of unclear gender. I agreed Tina was caring and generous. I'd seen real compassion in her eyes for Daphne and others. Unfortunately, she was also generous with sexual favors.

After Daphne left, I wondered if Tina had asked her friend to talk to me. If so, I supposed that was OK, because it meant Tina wanted to stay with me. Maybe the frat boy was just another one of Tina's charity cases—a tall, dark-haired, broad-shouldered, Nordstrom-dressed charity case.

A few days later, Tina and I smoked alone on the porch roof. At one point, I alluded to her childhood sex abuse.

"What are you talking about?"

"You know, your cousin."

"I never said anything about a cousin abusing me."

"What? Of course you did."

Blowing out cigarette smoke, Tina gave an incredulous laugh. Her eyes didn't crinkle like usual. "You're up in the night."

As a kid, I'd been fascinated by Sybil, the woman with sixteen personalities. I'd read much of the book at the library and watched the TV movie starring Sally Field. Sometimes Sybil couldn't keep track of what her other personalities told people. Could Tina have a split personality, like her roommate in the mental hospital? Sometimes she seemed like a vulnerable little girl, while other times she was cool and unflappable like Bugs Bunny, smoking a Marlboro Light in place of munching a carrot.

If Tina had two or more personalities, I wondered which one was telling the truth about the sex abuse. I started watching her for more signs of split personality. In time, I'd realize another Cabbage Patcher was even more mentally ill than Tina.

To mark the end of summer, Lisa rented a condo up near Park City. Chad brought high-alcohol beer from Evanston, Wyoming, where he also occasionally drove for stronger firecrackers and porn. I drank, but not too much. Before the night was over, I'd wish I'd drunk enough to pass out.

As weed and alcohol ran low, people started lying down to sleep. Tina and I couldn't find a spot big enough for both of us, not even on the floor. I rolled up a towel for my pillow and tried to get comfortable on the carpet near a wall. Tina squeezed between the foot of the bed and a guy I didn't know.

Deep in the night, I came out of a doze. As I lay in the dark, I heard rhythmic, fleshy squelches nearby, along with little gasps. Someone was having sex on the floor, just a few feet away from me. I propped myself up and tried to see, but I couldn't. However, I recognized Tina's sounds, and I thought I could even smell her. Lying back down, I willed myself not to stand up and cry out, "What the hell?" Soon the faint sounds crescendoed and then stopped. A faint giggle removed any doubt.

As I writhed on the floor, I tried to reason with myself. Why was I reacting like a stupid Mormon? Tina's sexual behavior was new wave—*I might like you better if we slept together.* Where was my decadence? Somehow, I needed to unbrainwash myself from wanting only one female partner who wanted only me. I needed to get chaotic neutral about sex. I needed to take whatever came my way, maybe even go out and get it like Matt and Chad did. I imagined myself cheating on Tina. If she caught me, maybe she'd say, "Now you're getting it!" But the idea of being sexually radical made me queasy.

I tried reviving my old fantasy about *Logan's Run,* a sci-fi movie I'd loved when I was nine. Through a biological broadcast system called the Circuit, anyone could have sex with anyone, male or female. When Logan beamed Jessica into his apartment, he simply said, "Let's have sex," and she agreed. In addition, the domed, futuristic city provided an orgy area called the Love Shop, where naked people groped each other in slow motion amidst pink narcotic vapors. Maybe we could turn the Cabbage Patch into something similar. Breathing our greenish-gray marijuana vapors, we could hold an ongoing orgy like the hippies did in their communes.

But then I started wondering who else Tina had screwed. The cocaine dealer, obviously. Any number of frat boys. A night manager down at Crown Burger? Was Matt still getting some action? Had Vince taken any turns? Chad had already used the Cabbage Patch as a love nest with two other girls. If he and Tina found themselves alone, what would stop them?

Maybe Tina was a nymphomaniac. Maybe she binged on sex like she did on food. I'd never heard her say anything about condoms or the pill. For all I knew, she'd already gotten one or more abortions or put a baby up for adoption. She'd told me her periods were irregular and she had something called endometriosis, which made her hurt sometimes. Maybe she was just conveniently infertile.

Tina had bargained sex to move into the Cabbage Patch, but I'd assumed she was also interested in me as a person. However, maybe she didn't feel that way at all. Lying on my back, I imagined her hovering over me like a succubus from Dungeons & Dragons, a demon who took female form to seduce men for nefarious purposes. When I'd made my saving throw against Tina, apparently I rolled a one on the twenty-sided die.

"He was so small, I didn't even feel it!"

"Oh, OK. I feel better now."

Tina frowned at me. Leaving the Cabbage Patch's kitchen, she went into the main room. I heard her rifle through the plastic bin where she kept her cassette tapes.

I followed her, my stomach twisting. "It's been a fun summer," I said. "But now you need to move out."

"No!" she cried. "I swear, I won't do anything ever again. You don't know how much bad stuff I could've done, but I didn't."

"I'll assume you haven't robbed any banks or murdered anyone."

When Tina started crying, I folded my arms and watched her. When she tried to hug me, I pushed her away. Just then, we heard people tromping up our back stairs. As soon as Lisa saw Tina's face, she turned around. "Come on, guys," she said to Matt, Maeve, and Janet. "We're going to the movies."

Sniffling, Tina turned on my stereo and put in a Police tape. The lead singer Sting was her guru. She'd even seen him up close when he'd used an exercise bike near hers, flustering her so much she had to go sit down. Whenever Tina played the Police song "Invisible Sun," she got all mushy and spiritual. To me, the lyrics sounded too much like Mormonism's light of Christ, which supposedly radiated throughout the universe. I liked the song's music but not the message.

Tonight, however, Tina wasn't looking for "Invisible Sun." She kept pushing fast-forward until she reached "Can't Stand Losing You." Turning up the volume, she sang along with Sting, right in my face: "I guess this is our last goodbye, and you don't care, so I won't cry. But you'll be sorry when I'm dead, and all this guilt will be on your head."

Chapter 6

LISA NURSED ME THROUGH MY LOVESICKNESS. SHE brought me food and took me to movies. Sometimes she just drove me around, trying to get me chatting about things other than Tina. She gave me hugs and backrubs, which I found mostly awkward. I wished I were as close with Lisa as Matt was. She'd saved him emotionally from his polygamous father and introduced him to freedom and fun. But when Lisa looked into my eyes to infuse me with emotional healing, I always looked away.

At first, Tina slept downstairs at the cocaine dealer's. Then she moved in with a frat boy, not the same one I'd caught her with. When the frat boy brought her back to the Cabbage Patch to get her stuff, she kept flashing me hurt-but-victorious smiles. I felt mostly sick but also a little relieved. I wondered how much she liked the frat boy and how much she was just using him.

During my Tina hangover, I listened to the Tears for Fears album *The Hurting* over and over. Maeve grooved on it with me. She didn't like most new wave—she especially disdained our silly B-52s—but she loved *The Hurting*. Janet took over the Murphy bed, and I slept alone in my childhood bed, rarely able to drop off until I'd either cried or climaxed.

The only other time I'd cried over a female was in eighth grade. One day, a ninth-grade girl hinted we could be a couple.

She was fourth on my crush list, and she wasn't a tomboy. I thought I finally had a girlfriend, but then I overheard the girl say something similar to another kid. At home that afternoon, I felt so confused that tears squeezed out. Later, I realized the girl's strategy was to put out hints to several boys and see who stepped up. She'd done her part, and she wanted someone to do his. But I had no idea how to play the male role.

The ninth-grader loved furry little pets. When her rat had babies, she gave me two. At first, I liked the rat pups. Their black-and-white fur reminded me of an orca. But within a few weeks, their cute, snubby snouts turned pointy, their tails grew long and scaly, and their testicles swelled obscenely. They kept smearing poop all over their glass aquarium walls. After they escaped and broke into my mouse's cage, I found the carcass chewed and headless under my bed.

One afternoon, I transferred the rats to an old wire cage, and a friend and I took them to a blocked culvert near our houses. Throwing the cage into the brown water, I felt thrilled but also queasy. As we watched, a few bubbles came up. My friend must've blabbed, because the ninth-grader gave me an outraged, grieving look the next day, as if I'd killed twin babies we'd conceived together.

I'd blown it with the rat girl, but I'd only been nice to Tina. I knew I never would've cheated on her. As I thought about her hapless new frat guy, I realized I felt a little sorry for him.

As Lisa continued trying to help me, she apparently decided turning me gay would cure me of Tina. First, she tried involving me with some deaf new wavers who held gay orgies, and then she tried hooking me up with a gay guy at a party. However, I rejected both. I liked girls too much to turn gay, but I started wondering if I could be bisexual, like Matt and other new wavers. Bisexuality would increase my options—I could take whoever pursued me, boy or girl. And bisexuality seemed to fit with my astrological sign, the balancing scales of Libra. In Dungeons & Dragons, I liked playing characters with dual races and classes, usually elf/human wizard/thieves. Why not take a similar approach with sex?

However, I wondered if I could handle the male side of the scales. I'd never had a crush on a boy, and I couldn't take them seriously as possible romantic partners—I'd felt more romance toward my female dog than I ever had toward any human male. And gayness had always felt sinister to me. Growing up in Los Angeles, I'd watched a TV report on homosexuality when I was only about five. At one point, the reporter had interviewed a chicken hawk, his face silhouetted and his voice altered. He sounded like a boogieman, lurking in public parks for innocent boys like me.

On the other hand, I'd already experimented with some boys. When I was seven or eight, I slept over with a nerdy kid who carried science gadgets on his belt. Up in his bedroom, he taught me a game called strip poker. As our clothes came off, we noticed a hole in my undershirt. Soon we were ripping apart each other's underwear and fondling private parts.

Later, the kid referred to our activity as sex. The TV report on homosexuality had featured two men who happened to share a bed one night. When they woke up, one man's leg was over the other's, and it felt good so they turned gay. Had the same thing happened to me? I hoped not. The nerdy kid annoyed me, and I liked him even less after the strip poker.

A few years later, not long before I turned twelve and would receive the Aaronic priesthood, I started feeling guilty about the strip poker. I couldn't remember if it'd happened before or after I was baptized at age eight. If before, then the sin had been washed away. If after, then I'd never repented of it, and I would need to confess. By the time the bishop interviewed me about my worthiness to receive the Aaronic priesthood, I'd decided the strip poker had happened before my baptism, and so I didn't mention it.

After we moved to Utah in 1977, I made a friend named Doug. He lived down in the older, poorer part of the ward, where some of the members seemed like Mormon hillbillies to me, with their shabby clothes and hickish manners. In sixth grade, as Doug and I goofed around in a school restroom one afternoon, he turned to me and said, "Let's be gay." At first, I thought he was joking— the word *gay* meant lame. But Doug's expression was real, a mix of resignation and pleading.

"I guess," I said. I knew something sexual had to happen soon, and I knew it wouldn't happen with any girls of my acquaintance, even if I'd had the nerve to pursue them.

After school, we locked ourselves in a mildewy trailer parked in the weeds behind Doug's house. Taking off our clothes, we started rubbing each other. Before long, I felt almost impossibly good down there, and Doug made a disgusted noise.

"Is that sperm?" he asked in an accusatory tone.

At first, I didn't know what he was talking about. All I knew was I felt a strange mix of relief and delinquency. Then I saw some milky goo on the upholstery. Had it come out of me? I'd imagined males controlled ejaculation the same as urination, but apparently not.

"How would I know?" I said to Doug. *Don't blame me,* I wanted to say. *You're the one who kept rubbing it like that.*

Grabbing a sock, Doug attempted to clean up. I tried to help, but the goo was elusive, like mercury from a broken thermometer. After a few moments, Doug threw down the sock, pulled on his clothes, ran inside, and took a shower, as if he'd been exposed to radioactive waste.

With some practice, I learned how to produce the same result on my own. Sometimes I thought about girls I'd crushed on or porn I'd seen, and sometimes I imagined a molester coming after me, which seemed a likelier scenario. Once, I dribbled honey on myself to get my dog to lick me clean, but it didn't work like I'd imagined. Later, I felt glad I'd failed. I'd heard about a guy named Rex who'd done it with a sheep—throughout Davis County, kids pronounced his name *Ree-e-x.* I didn't want people to start woofing my name.

During junior high, one of the Mormon hillbilly kids got a footlocker of porn from his long-haired, ex-Mormon, Vietnam-vet uncle. In a basement bedroom one rainy afternoon, a group of us flipped through the magazines. After a while, people started undoing their pants. I heard Doug call out, "No kissing!" *Eww,* I thought, *that would be so gay.* Then I dog-piled with some other naked boys, all of us squirming to get friction where it counted. Afterward, no one ever spoke of our orgy, and we never saw the porn footlocker again.

Later that week, my eye caught movement outside my basement bedroom window. Peering into the window well, I could see only wet, brown leaves. But then I saw a glistening tiger salamander, about six inches long. Clasped in my hand, his body felt moist, cold, and strangely heavy. Then I saw another black-and-yellow-striped salamander, and then another. I figured the rain must be flooding them out of their muddy lairs. Soon I'd collected seven salamanders in my aquarium, all squirming over each other. I threw in some mud and leaves, but I didn't know where to get bugs. A few days later, I found the aquarium littered with tiger-striped legs and torsos, like a scene of carnage from the Book of Mormon. I realized another orgy of involuntary animal appetite had taken place.

Lying in my bed in the Cabbage Patch, I felt squeamish remembering my past experiments. If I turned bisexual, I doubted the homo side could ever balance out the hetero. But even without Lisa's interference, I received only gay attention. At Crossroads mall one afternoon, a middle-aged man stepped up behind me on the escalator. "Know anyone looking for a job?" he asked.

I thought for a moment. The man looked clean cut and reputable. I was tired of the toy store—they'd recently suspected me of stealing cash from the till, which I hadn't done. "Maybe me," I said.

"Great." The man nodded and smiled.

"What kind of job?" I asked as we reached the top.

He gave me an odd look. "Uh, moving antiques."

"OK, cool. I gotta get back to work, but I'll give you my phone number."

Riding the bus home that afternoon, I suddenly realized the guy must've been a chicken hawk. I couldn't believe I'd been so naive. I reached up and touched the earring in my left ear. Had I misunderstood which ear meant gay?

When the man called that night, I said I wasn't interested and hung up. I couldn't imagine myself being voluntarily bisexual. But would I ever meet another girl with Tina's good aspects—including her forwardness—and not her bad ones?

Lisa was in love with Cleo, a new-wave girl from a Depeche Mode–obsessed clique originally formed at Brighton High School on the Salt Lake Valley's east bench. Cleo wore a tall, thick, platinum-blond flattop with a long, thin braid down her back. She walked around with haughty sophistication, like new-wave royalty. We knew frumpy, earthy Lisa had no chance with her.

Word came that the Depeche Mode people were planning a lesbian wedding for Cleo and another girl. As Lisa drove us to the event, we could tell she was wigged out, both proud and

envious. I was surprised how many people crowded into the
backyard, not only new wavers but also older people. A short,
chubby-cheeked butch performed the brief mock-ceremony.
As the two brides French-kissed, the crowd freaked out, and I
couldn't help thinking of the term *hubris* from A.P. English. Part
of me found the wedding daring and decadent, but I wondered
why any homosexual would ever want to marry. Didn't they
want to escape lifelong wedlock and childrearing?

As the afterparty continued, I enjoyed watching a cluster of
parents sip their beers, trying not to look bewildered. Lisa stayed
near us, occasionally wiping away tears. At one point, we overheard Cleo's new fake-wife admit she wasn't really lesbian. "I like
men too much," she declared. Lisa's face morphed into a relieved,
hopeful expression.

Once buzzed, I felt inspired to try turning Cleo hetero, or at
least bi. I could grow a huge, thick flattop to match hers, and
we'd be the coolest platinum-blond couple. I tried to coax her
into a bathroom, but she shook her head and glided away with a
pained look, like a queen who'd smelled a fart. Later that night,
some of us crashed in the basement, and I awoke to one of the
Depeche Mode boys molesting me. I wasn't into it, but I let him
finish the job.

The next time we went dancing at the Maxim, Lisa dressed
up in a strange new way, with a masculine pinstriped suit, frilly
white shirt, and shiny black shoes. Her hair was slicked back on
the sides and plumed on top, and she'd put on some makeup.
When Cleo came in later, Lisa knelt before her, took her hand,
and slipped a ring onto her engagement finger.

Cleo wore the ring for a while and let Lisa dance near her.
Before leaving the club, however, she gave back the ring. Lisa
didn't seem to fully recover for weeks. I knew I should've helped
her through her lovesickness like she'd helped me, but I didn't
know how. It wouldn't be the last time I failed her.

Chapter 7

ONE DAY IN SEPTEMBER, WE WENT DOWNTOWN FOR Rock Against Reagan. The U.S. president was in Salt Lake to speak at an American Legion convention. The punk protest took place on a plaza across from his hotel.

I considered myself anti-political. My earliest political memories were Vietnam, Watergate, gasoline shortages, and American hostages in Iran. When I was thirteen in 1981, I'd watched my mom weep during Ronald Reagan's inauguration on TV. The Mormon Tabernacle Choir sang "Battle Hymn of the Republic," and the Reagans wept too. But I didn't like President Reagan— people acted like he could heal America from the sixties and seventies, but to me he just seemed generic and robotic, like a Mormon general authority. I liked the punk art that called him "Ray Gun" and showed ballistic missiles bristling from his ears, eyes, nostrils, and mouth.

The protest bands included Public Nuisance, Maimed for Life, the Massacre Guys, and Avon Calling. I liked how punks often didn't applaud after songs—they expressed appreciation by yelling insults at the band, spitting at them, or slamming even harder in the mosh pit. But the sound system was awful, and punk didn't belong outdoors in the wholesome daylight. Between bands, a grim reaper moved through the crowd on stilts. One speaker claimed Reagan was OK with up to twenty million

Americans dying in a limited nuclear war. Wearing their goofy Boy Scout–esque caps, legionnaires kept stopping to gawk.

I related to punk's antiauthority, antigovernment attitude. If we didn't want Reagan as president, I wondered, then who did we want? Or did we not want a president at all? That sounded like the smartest option. Why should one human have so much power over so many people? I felt the same way about the Mormon prophet.

Vince came up to me. "The FBI has a file on you now," he said. "Why?"

"Just because you're here. They're taking photos of us."

I liked the idea of the government classifying me as a radical. I wondered if I'd ever do anything to actually merit it.

With Virgil and Tina gone, Janet took over as my Cabbage Patch roommate, though she still didn't have a job to help pay rent. I thought TV was lame, but Janet brought one in. She started scolding me for not rinsing my tuna cans. Whenever I heated canned chili, she made retching sounds. "It smells the same going in as coming out," she said. I wanted to say, "Why don't you pay your share by cooking and cleaning," but I didn't.

I was getting tired of the Cabbage Patch's squalor. As a kid, I'd been a neat freak. In my half of the bedroom, I'd kept the brown shag vacuumed and raked. Every week, I changed my sheets and cleaned our bathroom with Scrubbing Bubbles, which sprayed out thick and fragrant like shaving cream. I liked putting fresh, green-tinted shavings in my hamster's cage. For fun, sometimes I reorganized my drawers and shelves. In the Cabbage Patch, however, I was a slob. Occasionally Lisa tried to clean up, but it wasn't enough. We had no vacuum, so my bare feet always picked up gunk. We had no chemicals to clean the bathroom. We were always behind on dishes, trash, and laundry. To my knowledge, we never changed the communal sheets and towels.

Sometimes I wished Janet and I could become closer friends, like she and Matt were. They'd both survived bad childhoods. They could shop for hours at secondhand stores like Grunts & Postures, often bringing home bizarre vintage clothes, jewelry, and knickknacks, most of it probably shoplifted. At midnight screenings of *The Rocky Horror Picture Show*, they loved screaming the responses, throwing toasted bread, and shooting each other with squirt guns. But I didn't like shopping, and I could only stand seeing *Rocky Horror* once. Not only was it too campy, but I'd always hated audience participation.

One day Lisa drove a carful of us forty-five minutes north to Janet's house near Hill Air Force Base, so she could get some stuff. The murky house stank of cats and cigarettes. Her bald, pockmarked stepfather stood over six feet tall, wearing shorts, a filthy tank top, and an oxygen tube. His voice was hoarse and menacing, and I saw a couple of black gaps where teeth should be. When Janet was younger, this stepfather would grab her by the hair and whip her with a belt, and she hinted he'd also sexually abused her. But for some reason she'd still helped him with his oxygen tank and glycerin pills, not wanting him to die.

After getting her stuff, Janet asked her stepdad for money. He growled, but he gave her a twenty. She was following advice from a punk named Steve-O, who played in the Massacre Guys: "I'm a heroin addict at age nineteen. I live on the streets. I left a bad home too. See where it's gotten me? I'm sick most of the time. I can barely eat. All I want is a fix. Right now, Janet, your parents are your most important asset. Use them. Say to yourself, 'I'm using you to survive so I won't end up like Steve-O.'" Though Janet bugged me at times, I felt glad she found shelter in the Cabbage Patch. Compared with most of my friends, my rebellion against boredom and conformity seemed lightweight.

One evening soon after Tina left, my parents took me out
for a seven-course dinner at Ristorante della Fontana, an Italian
place in a repurposed medieval-style church. They didn't know
about Tina, and I didn't tell them anything. Usually they resisted
preaching, but my dad snuck in one thing: "Eventually, Chris,
you'll have to choose between your friends and the Lord." I told
the Cabbage Patchers what he'd said. For days afterward, Janet
kept squawking into my ear like a parrot, "Friends or the Lord?
Friends or the Lord?" as if I hadn't already made my choice.

On the first day of fall quarter at the U, Matt said, "It's college.
We don't have to go." Instead of attending class, we went bowling
at the student union.

I'd been dreading school. I'd been drinking alcohol and smoking weed, so my brain was probably mush. I hadn't read a book
in months. The idea of trying to study in the Cabbage Patch
seemed ludicrous.

Later that week, Matt said, "Let's move to California."

I thought he was joking, but he made a real-sounding case.
We could stay with his uncle in Glendale until we found an
apartment. Matt wanted to live way down in Dana Point, where
his family used to vacation in beach houses before his dad turned
polygamous. My family had often driven south as far as Laguna
Beach, but I didn't think we'd ever visited Dana Point. It sounded
too remote, maybe even closer to San Diego than to L.A.

"We could get our California residency and go to UCLA in a
year," Matt said.

"Hmm," I said.

UCLA sounded unlikely, but I wanted to get away from Salt
Lake and especially from Tina. She kept twisting my stomach by
visiting the Cabbage Patch to smoke and giggle with everyone.

Janet predicted Tina and I would soon get back together. The thought made me queasy, but I could see myself getting lonely enough for it to happen. Tina would come back if I let her, but then she'd just cheat on me again.

"Let me ask you something." Matt gave me a challenging look. "What would be the punk thing to do?"

He had me there. I'd heard of several Salt Lake punks and new wavers moving west to Los Angeles, San Francisco, or Seattle. That's what scenesters did when they outgrew Salt Lake, like Tolkien's elves going west to the Grey Havens.

"All right," I said. "Let's do it."

I visited Bountiful to say goodbye on Saturday, September 29, 1984, the same day as my eight-year-old sister's baptism. During refreshments after the service, I told my relatives I was heading to UCLA, though I doubted I'd ever enroll.

My dad asked if he could give me a father's blessing. Leaving the cousins to swarm downstairs, the adults gathered upstairs in the master bedroom. As soon as my dad shut the door, my mom started weeping. The men circled around me and laid their hands on my head. For some reason, Grandpa Bigelow pulled out a tape recorder and turned it on.

The priesthood hands felt heavy and warm on my head. As my dad spoke his blessing, I barely listened to the Mormon gobble-dygook. At one point, when he commended me for staying away from alcohol and drugs, I inwardly smirked. The Holy Ghost supposedly inspired blessings, but my dad didn't have a clue.

The following Tuesday, my dad and brother brought over the van to take my furniture home. The Cabbage Patch stank of wickedness, and Janet's big bras and panties lay scattered around, but my dad kept his face stoic and resigned. Before he left, he handed me two hundred dollars left over from *The Oracle,* a Dungeons & Dragons magazine I'd published during high school. He'd been saving the money for "your next business venture," as he'd put it.

I didn't feel comfortable leaving cash in the Cabbage Patch, so I kept it in my jeans pocket. The day before we left for California, Matt and I walked through Nordstrom, where the new autumn sweaters were on display. After having worn jeans and T-shirts for several years, I'd recently started buying nicer clothes with my KFC earnings.

"Come on, man, those are preppy." Matt watched me finger the wool and sniff it. "You won't need sweaters in California."

"I'm just gonna get these three argyles."

"We need that money for rent!" Matt almost shouted.

"It's my money, not yours."

The sweaters cost me almost half the cash. Matt wouldn't speak to me again until our farewell party that night.

In the morning, Lisa got us breakfast at McDonald's. Watching us eat, she looked worried, as if this might be our last real meal. When she dropped us off at the Greyhound bus depot, she gave us each a twenty. I figured we'd probably return soon. How could we survive in Southern California without a car?

"We'll do a Thanksgiving road trip and come visit you," Lisa said. Wiping her eyes, she gave us bosomy, overlong hugs.

Little did I know I'd be tripping for Thanksgiving too.

Chapter 8

I F WE'D HAD A CAR, WE COULD HAVE CROSSED THE DES-
ert in ten hours, but the bus took sixteen. Arriving in North
Hollywood, we discovered Matt's cardboard box had burst open
like a clothing-stuffed piñata. I helped him gather his things
from throughout the bus's cargo hold.

Matt had said his middle-aged bachelor uncle was a fun, easy-
going dude. When the uncle met us at the bus depot, however,
he seemed uptight. He told us he'd recently married a woman
with a sixteen-year-old son. "Things are different now, Matt," he
said. After a tense dinner with the new wife, Matt whispered to
me, "We gotta get out of here."

We liked the woman's son, though. Alex wore longish Jesus
hair, a white tank top, acid-washed jeans, and a gold cross. The
next morning, he pretended to go to school and then snuck back
home after his parents left for work. The three of us sat out on
the patio. Glendale was no Palos Verdes, but I loved being in
palm-treed California, with its sense of ocean nearness and its
constant potential for an earthquake or sonic boom. This was
home, not physically and culturally dry Utah. I wished it were
warm enough for the beach, but summer was gone.

"You guys must be Mormon, right?" Alex asked.

"Hell no," Matt said. Flipping his bangs, he gave me a warning look. He didn't want me blabbing about his polygamous dad.

"My family is, but not me," I said.

"One of my good friends is Mormon," Alex said. "I even went to church with him once. But my pastor—uh, he loaned me a book. Hold on, I'll be right back." Alex went inside and came back with a blue paperback titled *The God Makers.* "Turns out it's a really weird-ass religion," he said, tossing the book into my lap.

While the other two kept talking, I thumbed through it. My eyes caught stuff about Joseph Smith's folk magic and treasure hunting, how the devil started Mormonism, how the religion was pagan and occult, how Mormons believed they could become polygamous gods. According to the book, the *Satanic Bible* identified Mormo as the god of ghouls, which explained why Mormons were obsessed with genealogy and temple work for the dead. In Chinese, *Mormon* meant "gates of hell." If Mormonism were that interesting, I thought, maybe I would've liked it.

"We need to call on apartments," Matt said in his brisk parental tone. Back inside at the kitchen table, he spread open the *Orange County Register,* which we'd purchased at the bus depot. Holding back his bangs, he scanned the classifieds and eventually let out a sigh. "Only two roommate openings in Dana Point."

If Matt weren't set on Dana Point, I would've focused our search on L.A. County's South Bay. Not only had I grown up there, but hardcore punk had started there. Palos Verdes was out of our range, but we could've tried for Redondo Beach, Torrance, or cheaper inland towns near LAX, like Hawthorne or Inglewood. I wanted to get into the L.A. punk scene, but I doubted it reached as far south as Dana Point.

When I dialed the first number, no one picked up. On the second, a male voice answered. He said his name was Scott. As we chatted, I explained our bogus goal of establishing California residency so we could attend UCLA.

"Look, I'm in a tight spot," Scott said. "My roommate only gave me a week's notice. You guys can move in tomorrow."

When I told Matt and Alex, they clapped and whooped.

"He doesn't have to meet us first?" Matt asked.

"Nope," I said.

"What if he's a murderer?" Alex asked.

"What if we're the murderers?" I replied.

In the living room, Matt and I sat on ancient gold-velour arm-chairs. Behind us was a gothic-looking liquor cabinet. Matt raised his eyebrows at me: *What would be the punk thing to do?* It wasn't even lunchtime yet.

Alex stood in front of a large stereo cabinet. He didn't seem punk, but I watched as he pulled out Black Flag's *Damaged* and put it on the turntable. The fast, angry, clunky sounds of "Rise Above" filled the room. I'd heard lead singer Henry Rollins was so punk that he let other punkers beat him, stab him, and burn him with cigarette lighters. But Black Flag was my least-favorite Southern California hardcore band—I preferred Bad Religion, True Sounds of Liberty, Circle Jerks, and other bands with actual musical talent. KCGL played them on a Sunday-evening punk show called "Unrest on the Seventh Day."

At the end of "Thirsty and Miserable," Rollins's voice instructed, "See if you can find the key to your mother's liquor cabinet." As if robotically obeying, Matt stood up and opened his uncle's liquor cabinet, which wasn't locked. The colorful bottles stood in rows like fireworks ready to be lit.

Alex looked interested but worried. "We'll just get a little buzzed," Matt told him.

We began nipping from various bottles. Hours later, when his uncle got home, Matt and I were sitting half-drunk at the kitchen table, drinking coffee. Alex had vomited and gone to bed. Glowering, Matt's uncle told us to stay in the guest bedroom for the rest of the evening. Early the next morning, he took us to the Amtrak station.

As our train traveled south toward Matt's childhood memories, mine slipped past unseen on our right. I remembered how elite Palos Verdes had felt after Torrance and Long Beach, like the celestial kingdom compared to the terrestrial and telestial kingdoms. The PV peninsula rose above the South Bay's smoggy, viewless flatlands, with stylish Mediterranean homes, lush ice-planted slopes, and the blue ocean always visible except on foggy days. Our subdivision was brand-new, which triggered some perfectionism in me. Whenever we descended from the peninsula, I'd cringed at all the old, tacky, shabby cars, buildings, and streets. Why was most of the world so mundane and incompetent?

After sixty-five miles on the train, Matt and I got off in San Juan Capistrano. Shouldering our stuff in garbage bags like homeless people, including my large stereo and speakers, we trudged down a highway toward the coast, passing the backsides of hillside mansions with pale stucco, red-tiled roofs, and manicured greenery. Wherever sprinklers didn't reach, the grassy slopes were yellow. The blue-skied autumn day was warm enough to make us sweat.

Scott lived in the middle unit of a condo triplex, about a mile and a half uphill from the ocean. He opened the door with a smile, but he frowned when he saw our garbage bags. He was probably in his early twenties, with new-wave–ish black clothes but a normal haircut.

Stepping into the bare front room, I felt confused. Where was the furniture? Had we miscommunicated? Was Scott moving out too?

"Unfortunately, the furniture all belonged to her," Scott said. He glanced uneasily up the staircase. "In fact, she's still packing boxes right now. She's sleeping here one last night. Can you guys come back tomorrow?"

Matt and I blinked at each other. "I guess," I said.

Scott let us leave our bags in the condo. Back out in the sunlight, we walked down the Street of the Golden Lantern, admiring Dana Point's smug California gorgeousness. The spindly, mop-topped palm trees reminded me of Dr. Seuss. Across the horizon, the sky and ocean appeared sifted like sediment from light blue down to dark.

"We can just sleep on the beach," Matt said.

"Sounds punk," I said.

"Yeah."

Near the harbor on Pacific Coast Highway, we saw a Jack in the Box. "Let's get jobs in there," I said. Growing up, I'd liked their spicy deep-fried tacos. As gringo teens who could work daytimes, we got hired on the spot for $3.75 an hour. We would serve customers, not cook or clean with the Mexicans. Our apartment and job had come almost suspiciously easily, both on the first try.

Wandering around Dana Point's waterfront area, I felt disappointed. Except for one surfing place, the shops and restaurants seemed targeted to wealthy retired couples. Strolling on the beach, I enjoyed the familiar ocean sounds and smells, but I missed the sensory intoxication I'd often felt as a child. Sitting fully clothed in the sand, we watched wet-suited surfers ride waves. I'd ended up a snow skier, which seemed lesser. We tried smoking, but the strong breeze made it too hard.

Matt wore his favorite Maxim jacket, black with lapels, the fabric speckled with silver. Staring out to sea with his bangs flapping, he reminded me of the brooding guy on the cover of *The Hurting*. Was Matt regretting his choice to bring us here? Dana Point already seemed so boring.

Scott hadn't said anything about a deposit, so we blew some of my cash on dinner at the Jolly Roger. Back outside, we resumed our wandering. The darker it became, the stronger the wind and surf got. I wished I'd grabbed one of my new wool sweaters. I'd hoped moving to California would wipe Tina out of my mind, but for some reason I missed her even more now.

Finally, our legs ached too much to keep moving. We tried falling asleep in some beachside bushes, but we gave up after about an hour. We hadn't seen any cheap motels in Dana Point, so we started walking down the dark Pacific Coast Highway, in the direction of San Diego and Tijuana.

"My family used to stay somewhere over there." Matt pointed south. "Let's go see what that light is."

About a mile down the road, we found a little seaside motel. I had just enough cash left to pay for one night.

"This isn't very punk of us," Matt muttered.

"No. But breakfast is included."

The next morning, we hiked back up Golden Lantern. I half-expected to see our garbage bags sitting on the curb, but around back we found the sliding glass door unlocked, as Scott had promised. As we snooped through the house, bare except for Scott's large master suite, I wondered again how this new arrangement would turn out. Would we end up regretting it, or would Scott?

Chapter 9

SCOTT CLAIMED HE'D ONCE AUDITIONED AS A DRUM- mer for Oingo Boingo. In postcards and phone calls, I told people we were living with Boingo's drummer. In reality, we felt banished. We had no Maxim, no Indian Center, not even a mall. A couple of gringo new wavers worked at Jack in the Box, but they were still in high school. The girl was short, freckly, and scrawny, with hair naturally even whiter than mine. She bragged about snorting cocaine on her breaks. I managed to get a crush on her, but she never made the first move.

I felt hungry for punk. We saw punk flyers hanging inside the surf shop, but the nearest gigs were thirty miles north in Costa Mesa. At dusk one evening, we saw some spiky-haired, black-leathered, chain-draped punks walking through a parking lot, like savannah animals on the move. Connecting with the right punks would've changed everything, but we hesitated and they disappeared from view. We never again saw punks in Dana Point.

At Jack in the Box, sometimes we paid half-price for food, and sometimes we snuck burgers outside behind the dumpster and crammed them down. When we had money, we stopped at Ralph's for groceries. When we were broke, Matt stole raw food from the restaurant's walk-in cooler. On paydays, we splurged at waterfront restaurants. We whispered about dining and dashing, but we couldn't bring ourselves to be that punk.

At the top of Golden Lantern, we found a shortcut over a cinderblock wall. By that point in our daily uphill hike, we were exhausted. We'd collapse on the grass and smoke cigarettes, as if tobacco could energize us to climb over the wall. In the evenings, we lay on bare carpet and watched a tiny television Scott loaned us, living out Black Flag's gimmicky "TV Party" song, literally not having anything better to do. We'd wanted to radicalize our lives, but the opposite was happening.

One afternoon, I opened Scott's bedroom door to snoop around, assuming he was still at work. As I stepped into the darkened room, Scott yelled out "No!" from his bed. I realized he was lying naked atop his seventeen-year-old girlfriend, motionless like mating insects. I backed out and shut the door. My desire churned for Tina—I still couldn't go an hour without longing for her.

We loathed sitting and sleeping on the floor. One night, I saw a TV commercial for a furniture rental place. I told Scott we could split the monthly bill three ways. A couple days later, we arrived home to a houseful of furniture. The living room had a plaid sofa and armchair and a coffee table. The kitchen had a table and four chairs. Our bedroom had twin beds with a nightstand in between.

"He couldn't have picked an uglier couch," Matt said.

"Must've been the cheapest," I said.

That evening, Scott informed us we needed to pay for the smoker's insurance on the furniture. He didn't smoke, but he didn't try to stop us, although sometimes he and his girlfriend hinted we should try to cut down. A small part of me felt bad about our stink and ashes, but Scott was the one who'd let smokers move in.

Though still in high school, the girlfriend tried to act more mature than Matt and me. "You guys need to get real jobs," Scott would say. The girlfriend would nod, her expression condescending with concern. "Then you could get a car," she'd add, as if we'd never thought of that. "And you could start saving for UCLA," Scott would say.

"It's like they're our parents," Matt complained to me.

Scott drove a new little red Honda CRX. Occasionally he and his girlfriend let us squeeze into the backseat to go to a movie or the laundromat. Once, they invited us to a dinner theater to watch their friend perform. Another time, Scott got us a gig valeting at a rich Asian guy's massive warehouse party, and we earned good tips.

"He's just manipulating us," I said to Matt.

"Yeah," Matt said. "He's using our money to pay for that car."

Somewhere in my mind, I knew we were being unreasonable. But what were we supposed to do, start obeying Scott and kissing his feet?

A married couple managed our Jack in the Box, and Matt was the wife's pet. With his earring off and his bangs tucked up into his cap, he looked like a chipper Boy Scout. He was warm with customers and competent on the drive-thru. Between customers, he wiped surfaces and restocked supplies. In comparison, I was aloof and lazy.

One morning, a mystery shopper ordered breakfast at my register. She wrote me up for being robotic, and she recommended I no longer work the front counter. It was the husband's job to figure out what to do with me. First, he tried to persuade me to take over the restaurant's maintenance. But I'd watched the previous maintenance man, a mustachioed Mexican gent who didn't speak English. The work was dirty and greasy and the learning curve would be steep, so I declined.

For a few days, I worried I might lose my job. Then the husband said I could be the prep guy. All morning, I worked alone upstairs in a room with stainless-steel counters, chopping lettuce and assembling salads. I liked smacking lettuce heads on the counter to loosen their cores. The only thing missing was music.

One afternoon after work, I looked in the mirror and realized my bad hair was the problem. If I could get the right cut, cool things would start happening. Some punks or new wavers would notice us, and we'd connect with the underground scene. I'd finally get a girlfriend.

I decided to try a retro flattop like Chad's. Growing up, I'd always avoided short haircuts as too military. One time, my dad had buzzed my hair extra-short as punishment for sneaking out in the middle of the night. The bristly hair made my head look even bigger. But I hoped the right flattop would look good, like the photo of my dad's 1950s flattop I'd seen somewhere.

Matt watched me flip through the Yellow Pages. "Can't it wait till Saturday?"

"No," I said. "Right now."

"You're being irrational."

"I can't help it." I grabbed a handful of coarse yellow-white hair. "I have hair issues."

When I was born in Newport, Rhode Island, the naval-hospital orderlies had called me "Little Surfer" because my copious white hair stuck straight up. In junior high, when my metal shop teacher had demonstrated a micrometer, my hair shaft surprised him by measuring thicker than the Native American kid's. Whenever my dad cut my hair, his thinning shears would jam like a lawnmower in overgrown grass. I'd shriek, and he'd donk me on the head and keep powering through my thatch. After I turned preppy during my senior year, a younger preppy kept whispering to me, "Get a real haircut." But even after I'd moved into the Cabbage Patch, my dad still cut my hair.

The nearest barber was in San Clemente, six miles down the coast. As our bus approached, I saw that San Clemente was a real town, not a bogus waterfront for old rich people. Why hadn't we moved here instead of Dana Point?

The flattop turned out better than what I'd had, but it wasn't ideal. On the sides, my buzzed blondness turned transparent, showing too much pink scalp. Up top, the two-inch flattop looked unsymmetrical even after the stylist brushed it with gel and a blow dryer. The haircut was expensive, and I remembered Chad needed frequent barber visits to keep his flattop looking sharp.

While we waited for our bus home, a red vintage car pulled up. Two girls sat in the front. "Need a ride?" the driver asked. We climbed in back. At first, I thought my new haircut had attracted them. But then the driver said she'd stopped because Matt was so gorgeous. The girls were seniors in high school. Wearing a scarf over her short hair, the driver seemed matronly. Meanwhile, the other girl looked about thirteen, with acne, braces, small breasts, and amateurish makeup. Their radio played lightweight, commercial new wave like Duran Duran, Culture Club, and the Thompson Twins.

We started hanging out with the girls. At our apartment, Matt and the driver sometimes made out. She could be funny, but the other girl rarely said anything. In the backseat of the red car, we sat far apart. Sometimes she sneered at me, as if daring me to make a move, but even if I'd felt attracted to her, I would've waited for her to initiate something. Why couldn't I be man enough to impose myself on her?

At Jack in the Box, the managers had started scheduling me for occasional evening shifts. I'd become friends with a funny Hispanic woman who smiled big enough to show her gold-capped front teeth. She spoke passable English, and she sold pot. I hadn't been high since leaving Utah, but I didn't want to smoke dope alone. Matt still wouldn't try it, so I got the high-school girls to smoke with me.

After a couple evenings watching me giggle with the girls, Matt finally started smoking pot. Soon he and I were getting high every day after work. Lying bored on my bed, I'd revisit conundrums that had dizzied me as a child. I tried to imagine nothing existed, not even space—but what would take the place of space? Some kind of endless black solid? But that would be something. Why did there have to be something rather than nothing? Part of me wished there had never been anything, ever.

Chapter 10

WE REALIZED OUR COPY OF *The Hurting* WAS MISS-
ing. Sometimes, listening to that album was the only
way I could get through a Tina crisis. We assumed Scott had
swiped it when he took back his records we'd borrowed without
asking. We searched his room, but we couldn't find it. However,
I confiscated a pair of Army combat boots too punk for Scott
to own.

We hadn't noticed any record stores in Dana Point, so we
took the bus eight miles north to Laguna Beach. I already knew
this town—it felt almost sacred because my parents had hon-
eymooned there. On Sundays in the seventies, my family had
sometimes driven down to Laguna Beach between church meetings. My mom didn't want us swimming on the Sabbath, but
we'd played in the tidal pools. I loved poking my fingers into sea
anemones to pucker them shut.

Matt and I went halves on *The Hurting,* and then we explored
the seaside town. Laguna Beach had a cool, artsy vibe left over
from its 1960s role as Southern California's Haight-Ashbury.
Browsing earrings in a funky jewelry store, I purchased a tiny
silver man dangling by his ankle, his arms outstretched as if he
could break his own fall. As we licked cones in an ice-cream parlor, a man sat near us and started chatting. He seemed normal
and nondescript, a balding schlub in his thirties.

"How'd you guys like a real Hollywood experience?" the man asked at one point. "I've got tickets to a live studio taping of *It's Your Move*."

Neither Matt nor I said anything.

"You know, the TV show with Jason Bateman. He's some kind of high-school scammer."

"No thanks," Matt said. He kept his eyes focused on his ice cream.

The man turned to me. "We could hit Universal Studios too. And go out for a nice dinner."

Growing up in L.A. County, I'd longed to cross the parted Red Sea and see the animatronic *Jaws* shark chomp up from the water. But my parents didn't like amusement parks, so I'd never been to Universal Studios. Maybe this guy really did just want some company. My earring was in my left ear, so he knew I wasn't gay. Or maybe he was a chicken hawk. Either way, I felt desperate to do something punk, and this seemed like the punk thing to do, at least in some sense of the word.

"Sure, why not," I said.

Matt flashed me a strange look.

"I'll pick you up tomorrow night." The man smiled at me. "Tell me where you live."

Leaving the ice-cream parlor, Matt and I crossed the street to the beach.

"Do you know what you're getting into?" Matt asked.

I shrugged. "If something happens, it happens."

"Oh, something will happen. You can count on that."

I sat in the sand. Slipping off his shoes and socks, Matt wandered away. I felt surprised I'd taken the man's offer, but maybe a chicken hawk could help me forget Tina and stop aching for girls. Plus, I wanted to visit Hollywood, where L.A. punk had started. Just then, the chicken hawk plopped down next to me. I didn't know if he'd followed me or just happened to cross my path again. He started rubbing my shoulders, and then he moved lower. I felt embarrassed but tingly. A couple minutes later, Matt marched up and grabbed his shoes. "We need to go," he said to me, not acknowledging the chicken hawk. "*Now.*"

Arriving home, we realized we'd left our new copy of *The Hurting* on the bus.

I thought Matt would lecture me about chicken hawks, but he didn't say anything more. I wondered what would've happened if we'd both said yes. Matt and I were like brothers—nothing queer had happened between us or ever would. The next morning, I couldn't picture the chicken hawk's face. At work, I felt nervous and queasy. If I'd known his phone number, I would've backed out. The name of a Salt Lake punk band came to mind: Victims Willing.

The chicken hawk's car was small and old. As we drove north, he said he lived in an Arizona desert town and visited L.A. every couple months for some fun. "Now I've got another friend down here," he said. He patted me on the knee and left his hand there.

On our way up my dad's dreaded Harbor Freeway, I watched for familiar landmarks. I saw the Union Bank tower, where my dad had worked as a V.P. My favorite L.A. building was the futuristic Bonaventure Hotel, with its cylindrical, blue-glass towers that sometimes showed up in sci-fi shows. We passed Dodger Stadium, where I'd come closest to ever caring about professional sports.

As we exited the freeway, I asked the chicken hawk if we could get some alcohol, thinking I'd probably need it. He stopped at a convenience store and bought a six-pack of wine coolers. After a few sips, I didn't see the point—they were just citrus juice with a little white wine added. Our next stop was a burger place in a sleazy, run-down part of Hollywood. The male customers seemed mostly gay, and the chicken hawk seemed to know some of them. I could tell he enjoyed showing off his newest punk.

The motel room was smelly, with stains on the carpet and ceiling. The chicken hawk went into the bathroom for what seemed like a long time. Returning, he unzipped his bag, pulled out a small metal canister with a white plastic lid, and set it on the nightstand. The canister looked strangely familiar—I realized it was Crisco with the blue label stripped off. My rear puckered shut like a sea anemone.

The night was long, punctuated with moments of pleasurable biological friction. Once, I came close to vomiting when the chicken hawk slurped up my goop and pressed his slimy, horrifying mouth onto mine. I'd read about prostate self-massage and tried it a few times, but this was like a Mack truck compared to a golf cart. When it was my turn on top, I felt like I was trying to throw myself down the bottomless pit of the chicken hawk's digestive tract. At dawn, I escaped into the shower, grateful the chicken hawk didn't follow. Even with a soapy washcloth, I couldn't remove all the greasiness. I hadn't seen or smelled any fecal matter, but I could still imagine *E. coli* festering on me.

What bothered me most, however, was knowing for sure bisexuality wasn't for me. Somehow, I'd still have to connect with the right female at the right time. But Tina felt like a once-in-a-lifetime fluke—never again would a girl I could love make the moves necessary to bring us together. I wondered if Mormonism had brainwashed me into monogamous heterosexuality or I'd been born that way.

After breakfast at McDonald's, we wandered around Hollywood. In one store window, I saw a denim vest covered in punk patches, like a Boy Scout bandolier sewn with unearned merit badges. The Salt Lake punk scene was an offshoot of the L.A. scene, but at least punk was still underground in Salt Lake. Hollywood's commercialized punk was like blast marks left over from an explosion I'd missed.

As we drove to Universal Studios, I felt like I'd let the Child Catcher from *Chitty Chitty Bang Bang* lure me with free goodies. I'd prostituted myself in a cashless way, as I'd seen Tina do. The studio tour would've been fun when I was eleven. Sitting next to a chicken hawk at age seventeen, however, I felt bored, drowsy, and a little sore down below. I wondered how long the chicken hawk's rear had taken to get accustomed and why he'd kept trying until it did. I knew I'd never experience such a thing again, at least not voluntarily.

The nice dinner turned out to be Sizzler, a steakhouse chain so cheap my whole family could eat there. On the freeway back to Dana Point, I wondered how women could love men, especially older men like this chicken hawk. Part of me wished female chicken hawks existed and came after me, but another part viewed one-night stands as a sad way to live, whether homo or hetero. I could tell by the chicken hawk's creepy, over-the-top reactions to climaxes that he'd invested everything into his chicken hawkery. *Dude, it's not that great,* I'd wanted to say.

"Have you always been gay?" I asked him.

"Nah, I used to be married. But I'm through with women."

I almost asked if he had kids, but I realized I didn't care. Instead, I told him about Tina.

"Good luck with that, buddy. Here's the way I see it. No one owns anyone. If anyone wants to have sex, they should just do it. No games or complications."

I wanted to agree with him. It would've been coolly chaotic neutral, like *Logan's Run*. I wondered if promiscuity actually worked well for some people. I wished it didn't work so well for Tina. I wondered if she'd ever done anything lesbian.

In Dana Point, the chicken hawk pulled over and bought me two packs of Benson & Hedges Menthol 100s, a final tip for my services. When I arrived home, I thought Scott smirked at me, but I decided I didn't care if Matt had told him.

"So?" Matt asked.

I flopped onto my bed. "Not my thing."

"I could've told you that. If you were gay or bi, I'd know by now."

Even a week later, I thought I could still feel occasional Crisco twinges. I kept imagining a greasy, rust-smeared piston pumping in and out. And I'd started worrying about disease. During my senior year, AIDS had blown up in the news. I knew all about it because I'd written the topic summary for the debate team's extemporaneous speakers, including the fact that L.A. was an early AIDS hot spot.

Soon after the chicken hawk, a letter arrived from my Bigelow grandparents, calling me to repentance. Normally I liked these grandparents. One summer we'd lived with them in McLean, Virginia, while my dad attended stockbroker school in New York. Each summer during high school, I'd spent a week with them down in Provo, Utah, which seemed even more white-daisy Mormon than Bountiful, rampant with Osmonds, Brigham Young University, and American patriotism.

From pictures I'd seen, the young Avalon could've been a pinup model. She had dark, Mexican-looking features, none of which I'd inherited. She grew up in the tiny Mormon colony of St. David in the Arizona desert, near the old Wild West town of Tombstone. From what I understood, LaVell was the son of coffee-drinking socialist Mormons who didn't pay tithing because they didn't like how the church used the money. In December

1941, when LaVell was a pilot on the *Yorktown* based in Norfolk, Virginia, Avalon rode the bus out from Utah to marry him. Two mornings later, Pearl Harbor cut their honeymoon short.

I had to admit my grandpa was badass. In the Battle of Coral Sea, he'd aimed his dive-bomber at Japan's *Shōhō* carrier. When a Zero fighter locked onto his tail, he considered dumping his thousand-pound bomb and taking evasive action. At that moment, the Holy Ghost came into his mind: *You dummy! You have to hit that ship! Your country is depending on you. You will not be harmed in this war. Hold a steady dive.* LaVell stayed in the dive. No bullets struck his plane, and he scored a direct hit on the *Shōhō*. He went on to complete over a hundred airstrikes and receive three Navy Crosses.

In their computer-printed letter, my grandparents reminded me about my heritage. I was a sixth-generation Mormon. Twenty-three of my great-grandparents had crossed the plains as pioneers. I was a direct descendent of the apostle Heber C. Kimball. In the pre-Earth life, I'd proven myself as a valiant spirit. I'd been held in reserve to be born in these latter days. This life was a test to see what I'd do with my physical body, which wasn't a toy for pleasures or experiments but a tool to help me become like God, if I used it right.

Matt and I mocked the letter. I imagined the Holy Ghost whispering to my grandpa: *You dummy! Your grandson has run away from the Melchizedek priesthood and his Navy scholarship. Now he's down in California smoking dope and consorting with chicken hawks. Call him to repentance!*

I wadded up the letter and threw it in the trash. A few weeks later, the chicken hawk telephoned me and I told him I wasn't interested.

Chapter 11

SCOTT WENT AWAY FOR THANKSGIVING, LEAVING HIS bedroom door locked. As promised, Lisa drove down from Salt Lake, bringing Chad, Janet, and Vince. When I saw them, I almost cried with relief. Why had we ever left them? I felt glad Tina didn't come, but I also felt disappointed. If she'd come, I knew I would've tried to reconnect with her, probably on the floor somewhere. She would've helped dispel my chicken-hawk funk, but then I would've felt even more twisted up.

"Guess what, Biggs," Chad said, his flattop looking militarily precise even after the long drive. I hadn't maintained mine, so I was back to spiking my hair like a dandelion in seed. "I brought you some acid. Tonight you fry."

"You mean, like, LSD?" I asked. "The real thing?"

"Oh yeah, baby. I'd take some too, but I fried a couple days ago."

"I'll fry with you," Vince said.

"Are you really gonna take it?" Matt asked me.

"Maybe." I liked the idea of beating Matt to LSD, like I had with pot.

I turned to the two girls. "What about you guys?"

"I'll just get drunk, thanks," Janet said, giving me a concerned look.

Lisa avoided eye contact. "I'm already enough of a hippie."

I wondered why LSD was reaching me only now. Why hadn't Chad ever brought it to the Cabbage Patch? The more I thought about dropping acid, the more excited I felt. It was just a chemical, but it might be the closest thing to magic I'd ever experience. I'd always dug psychedelic weirdness, anything that got me out of the boring real world. As a kid, I'd loved closing my eyes, pressing my eyeballs, and watching the colorful spirals and starbursts.

Reading S. E. Hinton's *That Was Then, This Is Now,* I'd been fascinated by thirteen-year-old M&M and his bad acid trip, when he went down into his own stomach and spiders chewed on him for ten years. He kept trying to jump out the window, but the older hippies held him back. After the trip, he couldn't do schoolwork anymore, and he constantly worried about having a flashback. When he grew up, he couldn't have kids because LSD had ruined his chromosomes.

I wanted to test my brain against LSD. If someone took a drug he knew caused hallucinations, why would he believe they were real? If I ever dropped acid, I'd simply view the hallucinations like a movie's special effects. And even if I wigged out, I could get over it because LSD wasn't addictive. I hoped acid did scramble my genes, because I never wanted kids.

When it was nearly dark, Chad pulled out his wallet and removed a small wax-paper envelope with dark lumps inside. "Two hits apiece."

"No!" Janet cried. "Come on, Chad. It's his first time."

"OK, OK," Chad said.

"Purple gel's nothing compared to what the hippies took," Vince said, holding open his palm. Chad shook out two dark-purple nuggets, each a little smaller than a ladybug. Vince popped them into his mouth like aspirin. Then Chad shook one nugget into my palm. "Keep it under your tongue as long as you can," he said. As I tucked the LSD in place, I felt like the process should involve some kind of ritual or incantation. Matt and Janet watched me closely. Lisa had gone into the kitchen.

"Have a seat, you guys," Chad said. "It's gonna take a while."

My stomach fluttering, I sat on the sofa next to Vince. We were two astronauts about to blast off. "Don't let me jump out any windows," I said.

Chad and Vince both snorted.

"Surf's up!" Lisa called from the kitchen table. She'd set out an array of alcohol and mixers. It seemed quaint, compared to acid.

After a few minutes, Vince plucked one of the acid gels from his mouth. I thought he was downscaling to one hit, but he spread his eyelids and dabbed the gel into the outer corner, like inserting a contact lens.

"That's hardcore, Vince," Chad said.

"Doesn't it bug your eye?" I asked.

"It's worth it." Vince put in the other gel and sat back, blinking and squinting.

"Listen up, Biggs." Chad sipped his rum-spiked Coke. "Two rules of acid. No sex, and no looking into mirrors. I don't recommend eating anything, either."

Breathing deep, I wiped my hands on my pants. The gel had no flavor, and I didn't feel anything yet. I reminded myself that LSD was simply a chemical, not something sorcerous or demonic from fantasyland.

"You may feel a little nauseated at times," Chad said. "It's just the strychnine. It won't hurt you."

"Strychnine?" I asked. "Like rat poison?"

"Just a trace. It helps bind the acid to the gel."

Blinking hard, Vince stood up. "I'm out of here," he said. At first, I thought he was angry, but he smiled at me. "I gotta walk when I fry. Wanna come?"

"No, thanks." After so long without a car, I hated walking the hills of Orange County.

Lisa came over and rubbed my shoulder. "You sure, hon?"

"Yeah. I'll stay right here."

After Vince left, Janet sat next to me and peered into my face, like a kid waiting for popcorn to start popping.

When it was completely dark outside, Chad lit the gas fireplace. As the others got drunk and stoned, I kept scanning the room, watching for any freakishness. I wondered if my trip would be like the amusingly nightmarish tunnel sequence in *Willy Wonka and Chocolate Factory* or more cartoony, like *Dumbo*'s "Pink Elephants on Parade" song. I didn't want acid to turn me into a hippie—if it taught me anything, I hoped it would be cooler than "We are all one" or "All you need is love."

Like a nurse, Janet kept checking my eyes. I was starting to feel a little dizzy and shivery. Colors, lights, textures, and shadows seemed increasingly vivid. I moved from the couch to the fireplace, sitting down Indian-style and staring into the blue-tinged flames. With a drink in one hand and a cigarette in the other, Janet eased herself down next to me. "Don't forget, it's hot," she said.

"I see a little witch in there," I said, my voice softly amazed. Janet giggled, so I added, "Her name is Agatha."

As things started moving and melting and breathing, I crawled toward the armchair, which seemed like an epic journey. Everything looked curved and warped, with neon patterns and kaleidoscopes jumping out. Reaching the coffee table, I lost myself in its fake wood grain, which flowed like a river. Janet helped me sit in the armchair, her touch coldly electric on my skin. Her face moved with shifting colors, as if she were wearing animated war paint. "His pupils couldn't be any bigger," Janet called out. I tried to make a quip, but I couldn't speak.

I'd thought LSD would just affect what I saw, but chills and energy waves ran through me, with electric shivers shooting out to my hands and feet. Whenever I closed my eyes, the starbursts and swirls were crazier than anything I'd seen while pressing on my eyelids. I didn't keep my eyes closed for long, because I didn't want to miss anything.

As the trip intensified, it felt like LSD had flipped over a stone and released neon geometric bugs that marched, fluttered, and squirmed around me. At one point, my vision rotated frame by frame until I saw the world upside down. I felt occasional flitters of cramps or nausea, but other times my whole body felt orgasmic. The acid always kept moving—sometimes I didn't want it to ever stop, and other times I feared it never would. Occasionally I could sense an extra-dimensional being trying to push through the pulsing, shifting patterns. Sometimes this intrigued me, but one time it unnerved me enough that I cut off that line of thought, feeling relieved I was able to do so.

When my trip finally slowed down minutes or hours later, I realized someone had turned off the lights and the fire. Janet lay passed out on the couch, and everyone else had apparently retired elsewhere. Silvery light from the moon and streetlamps shone through the windows. Things I'd seen as moving creatures or machines were now a cluster of bottles on the table, someone's jacket on a chair, and a light fixture. At one point, I'd watched something pogo around the kitchen table like Tigger bouncing on his springy tail, but now it was just a broom leaning against the wall.

Marijuana had been about as cool as I'd expected, but acid was *way* cooler. It wasn't as badass as dive-bombing the *Shōhō*, but I still felt brave for taking it. Acid hadn't penetrated my innermost self, and I hadn't lost my connection with reality. It was like Santa Claus—as a kid, I'd let myself get caught up in the fun, but deep down I always knew it was just a game. As with pot, I felt disgusted the LDS church had kept LSD away from me. The church was always making promises about mystical inner impressions and burning spiritual sensations, but LSD actually delivered. The church wanted to keep everything cool away from us so we'd stay brainwashed and keep paying tithing.

After a while, the acid started getting freaky again. I clasped my hands behind my head and settled in for round two.

The next time my trip lulled, I realized my weird pelvic sensations were just a full bladder. Touching walls as my guide, I wandered through the psychedelic aftermath until I reached the bathroom. I didn't turn on the light, and I avoided looking in the mirror. Not trusting myself to stand at the toilet, I sat down. The seat felt unstable and abnormally cold. It took me a long time to start and to be sure I'd finished.

As the sky lightened on Thanksgiving morning, I heard the front door open, and a dark figure stepped in. For a moment I freaked out, but then I realized it was Vince. I'd forgotten all about him.

"Dude, how's your fry?" Even in the dim light, Vince's eyes looked bulgy and bloodshot.

"Totally good," I said.

He told me about hitchhiking all night around Orange County and meeting weird people. It was like hearing someone's long, rambling dream. Then he pulled out his little weed kit. "If we smoke a bowl, we can peak again."

I was exhausted—tripping was hard work. Part of me wanted to just go upstairs to my own bed, even if I couldn't sleep. But I knew Chad had probably taken my bed, so I went ahead and smoked with Vince. Sure enough, the acid soon kicked up again. My thrills came back, and things started undulating. We pointed out trippy things to each other. Once I got talking, I couldn't stop babbling.

☯

As Thanksgiving morning progressed, I wondered when my acid ride would come to a complete stop. Colors and contrasts still looked cartoony. I could still see halos and tracers. If I looked too long, busy patterns breathed or flowed. My depth perception was wonky, as when wearing new eyeglasses. I wanted to sleep but still felt wired.

Borrowing Lisa's keys, Janet took me for a drive. The sunlight was too bright, but it made the world look fresh and glistening. As Janet parked at an ocean overlook, part of me hoped she were making a move on me. Maybe she'd been the right girl for me all along. On the other hand, she was returning to Utah in a couple days, and I'd seen her flirting with Vince like usual.

As we smoked cigarettes, Janet asked questions about my acid trip, and I realized this was her purpose, not romance. I told her I hadn't felt paranoid or overwhelmed or scared or insane, which was almost completely true. I had not heard colors or seen sounds, though I wished I had. Time got weird, but it didn't stop or run backward. I didn't feel like I was melting, dissolving, or exploding, but I did see other things melt and explode. I didn't ever feel like I was being born or dying.

"Did you feel one with the universe? Unity with all living things? Perfect love?"

"Nah, no hippie stuff. Just an incredible ride. And by the way, 'Lucy in the Sky with Diamonds' is totally about LSD. I don't care if the Beatles deny it. The instruments and the lyrics and John's voice are right on, all shivery and spaced out."

"And 'Tomorrow Never Knows'?" Janet asked. "And 'Within You Without You'?"

"Totally," I said, trying to remember which songs those were.

"Someone should've stayed up with you." Janet gave me a regretful look. "I was going to, but I zonked."

"You should try acid," I said.

"My life has already been trippy enough."

As we sat watching the ocean, I remembered something else the itinerant preacher Lynn Bryson had told us. In the New Testament, the original Greek word for witchcraft was *pharmakia*. The scriptures spoke of sorcerers who cast spells using herbs, potions, and medicines. In today's world, recreational drugs were sorcery. Rock musicians took drugs so demons could inspire them to create spellbinding music, sometimes possessing their bodies so they could play their instruments with superhuman skill.

I liked the thought that LSD was modern-day witchcraft. I would've loved to become some kind of twentieth-century wizard or warlock. I also liked Bryson's idea of a satanic conspiracy in modern society, but I doubted demons and witchcraft were real. Psychedelic drugs were science, not sorcery. They simply affected the brain to see things differently, maybe even sense dimensions beyond the human physical. I knew reality must involve more than what I'd seen in life so far. I hadn't received any cosmic insights, but it was only my first trip.

By noon, my comedown was feeling queasy and anxious. The physical part wasn't as bad as an alcohol hangover, but the emotional part was worse. Everything seemed dull and hollow, and I wanted to escape again from my boring life. Would anything as amazing as my first acid trip ever happen to me again? I felt grateful LSD hadn't turned me into Mr. Hyde like alcohol could, with no memory of what I'd said or done.

Lisa wanted to make us Thanksgiving dinner, but everyone else wanted to go to Disneyland. Crammed with five others in Lisa's car, I focused my gaze out the window, trying to ignore the inane chitchat. Everything manmade seemed like an empty, dead shell. Everything natural seemed random and mindless.

As we wandered around Disneyland, I wanted to feel like a child again, but Disney was just another greedy corporation putting out processed crap. At nightfall, we splurged on overpriced Cajun food at the Blue Bayou Restaurant. Our table overlooked the dark, swampy prelude of the Pirates of the Caribbean ride. Watching the boats below, I kept half-expecting my white-haired, innocent, prepubescent self to pass by.

After dessert, Chad held up the little envelope with one LSD hit left.

"Vince?"

"Nah, I'm good." Vince yawned.

Looking at me, Chad waggled the envelope. I wanted to dive back into that otherworld. How many people could say they'd tripped at Disneyland?

"Sure, why not."

"Really?" Janet squeaked.

Lisa rubbed my back without saying anything. I didn't know if she were warning me, supporting me, or both.

By the time we got through the Space Mountain line, I should've been tripping, but I was getting only minor chills and visuals. For the rest of the night, the rides felt a little more intense, but the acid never really kicked in, my brain apparently still refractory from my first trip. When I finally fell asleep that night, my dreams were cartoonishly insane.

Chapter 12

A WEEK AFTER THE ACID TRIP, I COULD STILL SEE pulsing neon colors. Sweeping my hand, I could produce a tracer that lingered in the air. Smoking pot brought back the trip even more. I wondered if LSD had permanently changed me. Had I ever fully returned to my pre-acid self? I hoped not, but my life seemed overall as mundane as ever. When I asked my coworker if she sold acid, she hid her gold teeth from me. "You stay away from that."

After our friends left, Matt and I stopped pretending we had any future in Dana Point. We knew we were done with Scott, the Street of the Golden Lantern, and Jack in the Box. I hadn't ever thought I'd prefer Utah over California, but now I wanted to move back to Salt Lake. The city was big enough to be somewhat cool and small enough to be mine in a way L.A. never could, even if I had a car and lived in L.A. County. But I still hated Bountiful.

As a California kid, I'd loved staying with my Kimball grandparents in their cliffside luxury home high above Salt Lake's Avenues. At night, the vast, glowing valley sprawled like an upside-down galaxy. Utah's deep-powder Christmas snow enchanted me. Salt Lake City had more character than any of my L.A. suburbs. However, Bountiful was lame. When we moved there from Palos Verdes in 1977, it felt like we'd left elite, elvish Rivendell to homestead in the hillbilly Shire. Bountiful Mormons lived in cozy, grandmotherly-smelling brick bungalows and ate rustic foods from their basement storage rooms, like oatmeal, graham crackers, tuna casserole, honey, Jell-O, and raisins. Instead of Mercedes Benzes, Rolls Royces, and Bentleys, Bountiful was all station wagons, Chevy Blazers, and pickups. Main Street reminded me of *Happy Days,* a TV show about the 1950s. In Palos Verdes, my grade had included only two other Mormons, both of them duds. I'd wished being Mormon were more like being Asian or Jewish. My friend Joe invited me to exotic Japanese festivals downtown, but I didn't invite him to Mormon activities because they were too *Little House on the Prairie*–ish, like square dances and pioneer-themed parades through public parks. Joe had a two-foot-tall, transforming robot from Japan called Raideen. Being Mormon felt equivalent to being Japanese, but where was my Raideen or something equally cool?

One day on the playground, some kids decided we'd play four-square as Christians vs. Jews. When I said I was Mormon, they put me on the Jewish team, which was what I'd wanted. Nearly all the Jewish kids were Mentally Gifted Minors, and they were more sophisticated and humorous than Christians. At Hanukkah time, the school passed out little blue plastic dreidels, and I wondered why they never passed out anything Mormon, like a CTR ring reminding kids to "choose the right." When my mom birthed her fifth baby during Hanukkah, she left us a gift to open each day while she was hospitalized, and I told my friends Mormons celebrated Hanukkah.

In Bountiful, everyone was Mormon, including the bad kids. My first day of school, a chubby kid in overalls came up to me and said, "You can call me Chicken Beck 'cause I take care of the chickens." Another kid often came to school in farm-dirty boots and jeans. I felt particularly puzzled by a cross-eyed kid named Charlie Kingston. He rarely spoke, and every day he wore the same plaid shirt. Someone told me he was a "plyg," which I later realized meant polygamist. His eyes were crossed, I was told, because his mom and dad were brother and sister. Watching Charlie slink alone into a wooded area after school, I'd wondered if it were a shortcut or a hiding place.

When deer season came to Utah, the school had given us two days off. I'd felt astonished that people still hunted in the modern world. In the autumn-mottled mountains above our house, I heard distant pops and saw four-wheel drives crawling like beetles on a carcass. Boys and their dads wore orange hunting accessories everywhere but church, and we saw dead deer in the backs of pickups and slung over Blazer hoods. I was also surprised when my sixth-grade class attended the state fair, which felt like a throwback to the time of *Charlotte's Web*, whenever that was.

On Saturdays, I'd loved escaping Bountiful on the bus to downtown Salt Lake. We hung out in the two adjacent downtown malls, mostly the worldly Crossroads Plaza but occasionally the ultra-Mormon ZCMI Center, which even had a frumpy fabric store for Mormon housewives. After I'd turned new wave, my downtown headquarters had become Nordstrom's Café Express on the top level of Crossroads. We could sit for hours smoking, refilling our twenty-five-cent coffees, stealing croutons from the salad bar, and waiting for other downtown scenesters to pass through.

I even missed WORM, a grinning, pointy-goateed schizoid who roamed downtown Salt Lake in a bright-red devil's costume, his head shaved except for hair spiked into horns. Perched on the base of Brigham Young's statue, WORM would shake his pitchfork at passing traffic. One time he made the news by stripping down to his underpants and climbing atop Brigham's head at rush hour. He told a newspaper WORM stood for "World Order of Righteous Mankind" and his purpose was to caution us about our dark sides.

As Matt and I moped in Scott's condo, I couldn't get enough of X's song "Los Angeles." I listened to the song over and over, its zigzag opening chords like catnip for me. The girl in the song wanted to leave L.A. because she hated blacks, Jews, Mexicans, homosexuals, and rich people. I didn't think X hated these people and I didn't either, but I wanted to get out of L.A. too.

"Matt, we need to move back to Salt Lake," I finally said. We were smoking at our usual table in Jack in the Box. Matt's shift had just ended, and mine would start soon.

"Yeah, I know." He gave me a relieved look, like he'd been waiting for me to say it. "Rent's due in two days. Let's not pay it."

I called my dad, who immediately bought us one-way plane tickets home. Our Jack in the Box manager agreed to drive us to LAX. However, we didn't tell Scott we were bailing. After he left for work, we packed our stuff into cardboard boxes, including Scott's combat boots and several records. If possible, we would've taken his TV, stereo, and other stuff too. As we drove north, I felt a little guilty. Had we crossed the line from chaotic neutral into chaotic evil?

While I brooded in back next to a car-seated toddler, Matt and the manager chatted up front. Every time the kid squirmed or whined, I dreaded returning home to eight younger siblings. I wondered how soon I could move out again. We'd lasted less than three months in Dana Point, longer than the Cabbage Patch but still too short. I hadn't gone to any concerts or dance clubs, my one sexual encounter had been awful, and the few times I'd drunk alcohol had led to blackout and hangover. I'd enjoyed our fine dining, and I'd totally dug LSD, but I could pursue those in Utah—in fact, the LSD had reached me via Utah.

Diddling the upside-down man dangling from my ear, I fantasized about diving deeper into the Salt Lake underground. I wondered if I could create my own original style within punk, something to amaze other punks and scare the Mormons. Part of me hoped I'd see Tina soon, but part of me dreaded it.

Part 2

"There was fascination in surreptitiously staring at every creature we took to be a Mormon. This was fairyland to us, a land of enchantment, and goblins, and awful mystery."
—Mark Twain, *Roughing It*

"It is one of the triumphs of the human that he can know a thing and still not believe it."
—John Steinbeck

Chapter 13

ATT AND I SAT ALONE IN MY DAD'S BASEMENT office. Matt pulled out a cigarette and lit it. Tapping ash into his cupped palm, he gave me a teasing, defiant look. I'd smoked in his mom's house, so why shouldn't he smoke in my parents' house?

In California, my parents had kept a set of marble ashtrays in our living room. The mornings after grownup parties, I'd creep downstairs for leftover potato chips and onion dip and poke my finger into used ashtrays, enjoying the burnt smell. However, more than a decade had passed since they'd let anyone smoke in our house.

I watched Matt take a few drags. The damage was done, so I lit up too.

I'd been home from California only a few days. We'd been to the Maxim twice, but we'd lost the plotline after missing several months. I felt unexpectedly relieved to be back in my family's tall, boxy, rustically redwood-sided house with its steep front yard. But I also felt uneasy. My stuff reeked of tobacco and marijuana smoke. Snooping through my coat pockets, my ten-year-old brother had found black eyeliner and asked my mom why I had it. I didn't want to be like my parents, but I didn't want to influence their other children.

Tonight, I was watching my younger siblings. My parents had gone out for smothered burritos and a movie, and the other three teens were gone with friends. Before Matt arrived, I'd fed the five little kids the family's old standby of macaroni noodles mixed with ground beef and tomato soup. Then I'd put the toddler to bed.

Smoking in the basement, Matt and I laughed about what a dumbass Scott was. A couple days earlier, he'd called my dad to complain about his missing boots and records, the furniture he'd rented for us, and the money we owed him. After my dad hung up, I'd expected him to insist I make things right, but he'd just given me a puzzled look.

Just then, I heard a commotion from the stairs. Dropping my cigarette in the secretary's herbal-tea mug, I hurried over. At first, I didn't understand what I was seeing. Four kids were moving down the stairs as a group, all clinging to each other. The white-haired ten-year-old was moaning as if in pain, and the younger three were squealing and crying. I realized they were trying to hold back the ten-year-old, whose face was red and tearstained.

When the ten-year-old saw me, he roared and lunged forward with a butcher's knife. Instantly I understood. The boy had smelled our smoke upstairs. He knew smoking was one of the evilest things a person could do, so now he was going to kill me. Part of me wanted to burst out laughing, but I also felt bad. When I'd turned sixteen and become a priest, I'd baptized this little brother. Even then, he'd seemed skeptical about me, and now I was proving him right.

I gripped my brother's forearm with both hands, neutralizing the knife. I lied that only Matt had been smoking, and I swore I'd never let friends smoke in our house again. Eventually he dropped the knife and sniffled his way back upstairs. I couldn't imagine feeling that passionate about something. If I'd caught an older brother smoking, I would've felt shocked but also intrigued. I wouldn't have confronted him about it.

As we smoked outside in the frozen December air, I turned to Matt. "We need to get an apartment. Like, now."

A few days later, I inadvertently got revenge on Matt for upsetting my family. On our way to the Maxim, we stopped downtown at a tower where Matt and his siblings cleaned the offices of an LDS church–owned insurance company. While Matt vacuumed, emptied trash, and yelled at kids, I sat at someone's desk. Bored, I rolled a sheet of letterhead into the electric typewriter and filled a page with deviant, punkish, acidy thoughts. When the family was done cleaning, I turned off the machine but left in the paper. Matt's mom got chewed out, but luckily the family didn't get fired.

To my surprise, Janet was still squatting in the Cabbage Patch. For the past several months, no one had collected rent or shut off the electricity. On the kitchen counter, I found a pile of mail addressed to me, including several flat, square boxes from the Columbia Record and Tape Club. I wrote REFUSED on them and sent them back.

Matt and I didn't want to move back into the Cabbage Patch. By unspoken agreement, I took the lead in finding a new place. Matt's Dana Point attempt had failed, so now it was my turn. I wanted us to reach a new level of coolness. The best things I'd ever experienced were Dungeons & Dragons, punk, and LSD, and I wondered if I could somehow combine the three. When I imagined roleplaying punk-style wizards and warriors while frying on acid, it seemed so cool I thought the top of my head would buzz open.

I decided to focus my search in the Avenues, Salt Lake's coolest district. Janet and Lisa agreed to be our roommates. On our way to the Maxim one night, the four of us met a landlord at an 1893 brick mansion on the southwest corner of P Street and Third Avenue. Even though we stank of fresh-smoked pot and Matt and I were wearing eyeliner, the landlord rented us the ground floor. My dad loaned me my share of the deposit. I felt psyched, but I dreaded getting another crap job—of the four of us, only Lisa had income.

Our new place had just three rooms, but they were spacious. The ceilings were high, the floors scuffed hardwood, and the walls painted bright pink. I wondered if the banker, doctor, or lawyer who'd originally built the house had been Mormon or gentile. As I assembled my childhood bed, I hoped something interesting would happen on it. Ever since I'd gotten chicken-hawked in Hollywood, I'd felt skittish about sex, but I wanted to get back into it. Matt brought a mattress and an old-fashioned green sofa from his grandma's. Janet slept on the sofa, but Lisa never really moved in, driving home to Bountiful most nights.

One day Lisa brought over four new wavers who'd escaped from Tremonton, a small town on Utah's northern border. Their favorite song was "West End Girls" by the Pet Shop Boys. Before long, the jobless foursome had moved their mattresses into our place for a nonstop slumber party. Matt got into a relationship with one of the guys, who bragged about wealthy boyfriends but never had any money. He would later serve time in prison and die of an overdose. I let one of the girls grope me, but I didn't find her attractive. Before long, everyone's clothes were tossed in one big, colorful salad on the bedroom floor.

At some point, someone set out a stack of gay porn, the apartment's first and only reading material. I flipped through some magazines to compare my anatomy, but soon the porn made me squeamish, like eating a type of food I'd previously vomited.

Male erections looked ugly and painful. I agreed with what my mom had once said, during family showers after the beach: "Girls are better than boys because their units don't stick out."

On Sundays, we listened exclusively to Virgil's Beatles albums, which Janet had hidden in the Cabbage Patch so Virgil couldn't take them home. I felt zero interest in anything pre-Beatles, but the Beatles deserved our Sabbath worship as the counterculture's founding prophets. Growing up, I hadn't heard much Beatles. My parents had listened to classical music, the hippie musicals *Hair* and *Jesus Christ Superstar*, and bands like Chicago, ELO, Fleetwood Mac, the Carpenters, and Billy Joel. However, my mom had disliked the Beatles. Confirming Ringo's fear, she complained some of their singing was out of tune. She also distrusted their spiritual influence.

The preacher Lynn Bryson had badmouthed the Beatles even more than my mom did. According to Bryson, John Lennon was a sorcerer whose goal was to acquire the ancient spear used to stab Jesus during the crucifixion. Sorcerers like Lennon believed whoever possessed this Spear of Destiny would rule the world. According to Bryson, a human was sacrificed at John and Yoko's druid-witchcraft wedding, and the couple quaffed the person's blood. Eventually, Lennon's bargain with the devil had come due, and the devil dispatched a crazy guy to murder him.

One Sunday afternoon while "Yellow Submarine" was playing, we named our pink-walled apartment the Pink Submarine. The name made me think of an English punk band called Subhumans and the Sex Pistols' song "Submission," about their submarine trip with a girl they'd picked up on their TV screen, like in *Logan's Run.* As we sat smoking in the Pink Submarine, it felt like we were on a submarine mission through the underground.

Whenever Thomas Dolby's song "One of Our Submarines" played on KCGL, we sang along with it.

Before long, the name shrank to just the Sub. Outside the Sub, everything was ice and snow, but we were cozy inside our smoky lair, feeling "underground like a wild potato," in the words of our B-52s. We didn't watch TV or follow news. With no clocks or calendars, we often didn't know the day, date, or time. Some of us rarely even left the house. Lisa equipped the kitchen with mismatched thrift-store dishes, but sometimes all we ate was watery mac and cheese or instant potatoes, made without milk or butter.

After a few weeks, one of the Tremonton guys started shoplifting provisions for the Sub. Wearing a big black trench coat, he'd come home with an entire roasted chicken or carton of cigarettes. He insisted on keeping the cigarettes in the freezer, as if they might last long enough to go stale. He stole Camel Filters, so I switched to those from Benson & Hedges Menthol 100s. I was tired of menthol anyway.

Hiding out in the Sub and receiving stolen goods, I felt like Fagin from *Oliver Twist*. I looked a little Dickensian too, wearing my dad's old tweed overcoat and a pair of fingerless gloves. I hadn't put anyone up to stealing, so I didn't feel guilty about that. The Sub was way more fun than Dana Point, but sometimes I felt uneasy, like everything was going to fall apart. We were underground, but we still needed to get some cash flowing, one way or another.

The Tremonton people loved acid. I begged Matt, Janet, and Lisa to trip with us, feeling like Lucy coaxing her siblings to climb through the wardrobe. Matt finally caved—I'd been right about pot, and he'd seen me do OK with acid. However, Janet and Lisa still wouldn't.

Tripping, Matt acted like a befuddled old man. "Now wait," he'd say, staring at something throbbing or bouncing or melting. "That's not right. What are you wacky teenagers up to now?" While we were frying, Chad played freaky tricks on us. In the middle of talking, he'd silence his voice but keep moving his lips. Once he laid me on the floor and did some manipulations that made my body feel like it was melting down through the floor, into the literal underground.

On LSD, the Tremonton people called themselves fry babies. They giggled and shrieked too much. Like kids in a haunted house, we moved back and forth through the Sub, calling out new freakishness everywhere. Sometimes we thought we'd somehow wandered into neighboring houses, though we hadn't exited the Sub. We would've gone outside on fry walks, but it was too frozen.

Like a preschool teacher, Lisa brought us bubbles, crayons, water paints, and cheap toys, and she taped up our psychedelic artwork. Once she brought us Pop Rocks, but the candy sizzled too powerfully on our tongues, making our heads feel like they might explode. Sometimes we turned out all the lights and used our glowing cigarettes to draw orange lines that magically lingered. I thought of the picture book about Gus the firefly, who could spell out glowing words that stayed in the air.

One night, I broke Chad's rule and stared at myself in the Sub's bathroom mirror. Patterns, colors, and shadows crossed my face, and my acne flared and bubbled. For a moment, I wasn't even sure I was seeing myself. When I touched my cheek, the skin felt wet though I knew it was dry. After less than a minute, I broke away, not wanting to start clawing off my own face like the guy in *Poltergeist*.

After my seventh LSD trip, one of the Tremonton guys congratulated me. "You're now considered legally insane," he said. "You can never testify in court. They could commit you right now, if they wanted."

"If the FBI does a spinal tap on you," one of the girls said, "they'll know you've taken LSD. And it's stored in your fat. When your body burns it, you'll have a flashback."

"Sounds good to me," I said. I loved the idea of mainstream society declaring me legally insane, and I hoped I wasn't too skinny to have flashbacks.

At times, I wished we could go deeper into psychedelia. I didn't want us to become some kind of murder cult, but the Manson family's LSD trips had sounded cool. They'd all think the same thought at the same time. They could see themselves in each other's faces, like a mirror. When someone whispered in one building, others could hear it in a separate building. I loved how acid opened their minds to secret messages in Beatles songs. When I listened to the same songs while frying, no messages came through for me.

After one particularly intense trip, I made Lisa drive me to the Salt Lake Public Library to read about acid. I found the brain chemistry opaque, but I dug reading about the drug's history. The Swiss scientist who'd synthesized LSD while trying to develop a heart medicine said he'd felt a "peculiar presentiment" about it. "I did not choose LSD," Albert Hofmann stated. "LSD found and called me." Of his first, accidental trip in 1943, he wrote, "A demon had invaded me, had taken possession of my body, mind, and soul. I was taken to another world, another place, another time."

Cool, I thought. I didn't believe in demons, but part of me wished they could become real through acid. Every time I took acid, I felt like something new and unprecedented would manifest, something real in the physical world beyond hallucination, something that would remain after the chemical wore off. So far, however, it had not yet materialized.

Chapter 14

I T DIDN'T TAKE LONG FOR MAEVE TO COME ABOARD THE Sub. I'd missed the impish punk glint in her eye. I loved hearing her raspy, raucous laugh again—somehow, she even laughed with a British accent.

I wondered if Maeve had a past, present, or future in any normal sense. She was so punk, she didn't seem to desire anything. She didn't want to be in a band. She didn't seek employment or money. She didn't keep up with TV, movies, magazines, or books. She wanted nothing beyond coffee, music, conversation, and cigarettes. She liked hanging out at diners like Bill and Nada's Cafe, a 1950s throwback where gnarly punks ate eggs with calf brains. Maeve drank some alcohol but didn't seem to do weed or acid. I wondered about her sex life.

When Tina started showing up, I could tell she wanted to get back with me, probably so she could move into the Sub. But Maeve bristled whenever Tina came around. While Maeve was ultra-punk, Tina couldn't be less punk. I found myself taking Maeve's side. Tina gave me longing, incredulous looks. *Really? You choose this punk bitch over me?*

"Do you even like that twat?" Maeve asked me one night, after Tina left.

"No," I replied, only halfway truthfully.

The next time Tina came over, Maeve kept glaring at her. At one point, when Tina said something inane and let out a piercing giggle, Maeve stood up and pointed to the door. "My head can't take this anymore," she growled. "It's time for you to go." Janet and Lisa tried to soften it, but Tina couldn't get the hurt look off her face. She slunk out, and she didn't visit the Sub again. I hoped she felt some of the gut twisting she'd caused me.

Maeve began sleeping at the Sub, and soon her punk friend Eric joined us too. Down in the Sub's dirt-floored basement, Eric cleared decades of junk from the large furnace room and set up his bed freestanding like an altar. He had cystic acne like me, so he shared his Accutane prescription, and when the pills dried out my lips, I helped myself to his Carmex too. Sometimes I covered my acne with someone's face powder.

"I like having a basement punk," Matt said.

"Every house should have one," I said.

Eric had been in a band called Torn Between. He told stories about living in punk houses around Salt Lake. He'd stayed in the gray apartments by Cosmic Aeroplane, where the stucco-textured walls always breathed, even when you weren't tripping. He'd lived in the Hollywood apartments, where punks Helter Skelter–ishly spray-painted KILL PIGS on an outside wall. A retired hooker had lived next to them, poking punks awake each morning with her cane until someone got up to buy her beer. Other Salt Lake punk houses included the Zoo, Hell House, and the Slum. I hoped the Sub could become some kind of punk house.

One frozen but sunshiny day, most of the Sub denizens took the Third Avenue bus down to Crossroads to beg for spare change. I refused to try panhandling and Maeve wasn't in the mood, so the two of us stayed home, chatting and smoking on Matt's old green sofa. At one point, Maeve turned to me and said, "I like how you carry yourself." Then she stood up and held out her hand. "Come on."

She led me downstairs to the basement punk's altar-bed. Leaving our clothes on, we got under the covers. The room's only light came from a tiny window and the flame of the gas furnace. With no walls nearby, I felt like we were floating in a subterranean lake. Once we were settled, Maeve lit a cigarette. She took a drag, put her mouth onto mine, and blew smoke into my lungs. "Now back to me," she murmured.

The game seemed childish to me, like Patricia teaching me to clap out "I love you," but it still made me tingle. After a few exchanges, I eased my hand between Maeve's legs. To my surprise, she clamped her thighs shut. Realizing I should've started up higher, I reached for one of her small breasts, but she didn't allow that either. As if triggered by my frustration, the nearby furnace roared awake with hellfire.

Back upstairs in the Sub's pink-walled daylight, I felt relieved to finally have a girlfriend again. But it was weird seeing Maeve's soft, lovey-dovey side—there'd been nothing punk about that girl in the bed. If we weren't going to have sex, what was the point of making out? When it came to sex and drugs, both Tina and I were punker than Maeve. I wondered if she might even still be a virgin.

As Christmas of 1984 bore down, I hated sappy new-wave Christmas music but loved anti-Christmas punk rock. Spending Christmas in the Sub would've been the punk thing to do, but everyone went home except the two Tremonton girls. On Christmas Eve, my dad picked me up for our traditional pizza dinner, minus my mom. She would spend all night working on her sewing machine, and even then some unfinished gifts would contain sewing pins. I usually received a homemade flannel shirt, in addition to store-bought gifts.

Late the next morning, while my family was still occupied with Christmas, I slipped downstairs to my old basement bedroom. Another kid now occupied it, but my cardboard boxes still sat in the closet. I pulled out a certain box and slit open the packing tape. Inside were the holy artifacts of Geddy and Gygax, the two prophets of my early teen years. Geddy Lee was the singer of Rush, and Gary Gygax was the guru of Dungeons & Dragons.

I missed my roleplaying days. The Sub got boring sometimes, and I wondered if I could get anyone to play D&D. In 1979, I was the first kid in my Bountiful neighborhood to discover the game, via my Seattle cousins. As soon as I got the blue-boxed basic set, I started recruiting friends. Some couldn't take D&D seriously, but three guys got deep into it with me. All through ninth grade, we played every day after school, rotating who served as dungeon master. I put all my energy into D&D—when we weren't playing, I fantasized about it during school and church. As far as I knew, no one else at Bountiful Junior High was aware of the game.

Around that time, the media turned against D&D. The worst was Tom Hanks starring in the TV movie *Mazes and Monsters*. After hallucinating he'd killed a monster, the Hanks character went crazy and turned permanently into his game self. To win, he believed he had to cast a certain spell while jumping off the south tower of New York's World Trade Center. His friends managed to stop him, but he never fully recovered from his psychosis. I couldn't believe how many people thought the movie depicted a realistic danger. Our parents didn't seem aware of the anti-D&D hype, but the traveling preacher Lynn Bryson almost ruined everything. He claimed D&D was a clandestine recruitment tool used by Satan worshippers and witch covens, with the game conditioning us to cast spells and interact with evil spirits in real life. I secretly wished D&D taught us actual rituals for casting spells and summoning demons, but of course it didn't.

After Brother Bryson's harangue, our parents asked if they could watch us play Dungeons & Dragons. My friends and I shrugged at each other. "Sure," I said. "But you'll be bored." Our group was barebones, using only dice, paper, manuals, and a chalkboard for sketching maps. Live-action roleplaying in costumes sounded goofy to us, and we felt no desire to paint fantasy figurines. But just in case, I hid the demon-filled *Monster Manual* and any fantasy novels and magazines with covers showing naked women, usually painted by Frank Frazetta or Boris Vallejo.

Demons didn't enter our gameplay much, but sometimes we discussed D&D's infernal aspects, especially the angel-turned-devil Asmodeus. The gods had created Asmodeus to hold back the demons of the Abyss so the gods could focus on making planets and creating intelligent mortals. When Asmodeus started trying to become a god too, the gods cast him out from the Upper Planes. Falling to the Lower Planes, he became master of hell. The story reminded us of the Mormon Lucifer/Satan, but our parents didn't need to know that.

Our parents also didn't need to know about our occasional use of Book of Mormon elements, like the time I named my D&D character Kishkumen. The other players recognized the name but didn't remember who Kishkumen was—only the dungeon master knew my true identity as a chaotic-evil assassin. In the middle of the night, I killed all the other characters and took their treasure and magic items. It was a blast, but my friends were pissed. I suggested they all create evil characters too, and we could be like the ultracool Gadianton Robbers with their lawful-evil "secret combination" of oaths and signs. But my friends didn't go for it, so I stuck with chaotic neutral. My characters continued to disregard rules, traditions, and authority. I didn't hurt other beings just for fun, malice, or excessive power or riches, but I did what was needed for my own reasonable success. If that included some lying, stealing, or killing, so be it.

In case our parents followed through and watched us play Dungeons & Dragons, I started preparing a lawful-good adventure so our characters could do something righteous and heroic. Maybe they could help a human settlement make peace with the band of elvish thieves infesting the surrounding forest. Our characters would organize an attack only if negotiations failed. We'd save women and children. We'd cover our expenses and donate any remaining spoils to the human settlement.

After Lynn Bryson, my parents poked their heads into my bedroom more often, but they never came in and watched. Whenever they checked us, we were always gathered around the chalkboard, rolling polyhedral dice and consulting manuals, maps, and statistical tables. It looked more like homework than a game—and it did make us smarter, including our vocabularies. When a teacher told me *extant* wasn't a word, I showed her the dictionary entry: "still in existence." Within days, the high school transferred me into honors English and American History classes.

I later learned Gary Gygax was a Jehovah's Witness who didn't celebrate Christmas because it was too pagan.

Setting my D&D stuff aside, I browsed through my old Rush albums. My eye caught *Permanent Waves,* my first and favorite Rush album, the one I felt best balanced their geekiness and prowess. I'd spent hours staring at this album's sepia-toned cover, which showed a gorgeous woman walking amid hurricane destruction with her skirt blown up, revealing strangely baggy white panties. Now I realized why the woman was smiling: her own witchy power had caused the hurricane. The woman was Tina, and I was the hapless guy in the background watching her, unaware of the massive ocean wave about to hit him. Rush had been trying to warn me.

Lynn Bryson had included Rush in his list of satanic rock bands. The big red star on the cover of *2112* was essentially a pentagram, and 2 + 1 + 1 + 2 equaled 6, an obvious reference to 666. The letters in *Rush* stood for "Rulers Under Satan's Hand," just as *Kiss* stood for "Knights in Satan's Service" and *AC/DC* meant "Anti-Christ Devil's Children." Bryson also claimed Rush's song "Vital Signs" promoted bisexuality: "Everybody need reverse polarity. Everybody got mixed feelings about the function and the form. Everybody got to deviate from the norm."

I'd loved Rush's longhaired, kimono-wearing, fantasy-and-sci-fi weirdness up through *Signals*. But recently they'd tried to turn new wave. Instead of progressive metal, the music had become embarrassingly synthesized and sappy. Abandoning their stoner-geek mystique, the three band members now wore short haircuts and trendy clothes. If they had to change, I wished they'd taken the punk or thrash-metal route. With their extreme skills, they could've gone faster, harder, and darker. Instead, they'd left that territory to cooler bands like Metallica, Slayer, and Dirty Rotten Imbeciles, which I heard on underground radio shows.

After Christmas dinner, I took my D&D stuff to the Sub. However, I left my Rush records home, not wanting to be mocked. Fantasy roleplaying would be extra-trippy if we played stoned or frying—maybe we could even hallucinate realistic monsters and demons.

Chapter 15

KCGL'S SLOGAN FOR THE NEW YEAR WAS "STAY ALIVE in '85." If I had any goal, it was just to keep getting freakier. However, my box of Dungeons & Dragons stuff sat unused. I couldn't find the mojo to launch a campaign—it would've taken too much mental effort, especially when we were high. Besides, living in the Sub already felt like a bizarre roleplaying scenario.

One bright, icy January midmorning, Maeve and I got up from my childhood bed, which we shared sexlessly. Stumbling into the living room, we found the others playing with a Ouija board. I'd never seen one before. It looked simple and old-fashioned, like an alphabet primer from pioneer times. To me, the Ouija board had always just sounded like a glorified Magic 8 Ball toy.

Lynn Bryson had warned us that Ouija boards worked. Evil spirits could communicate through them and mess with our heads. Most kids who got into the occult started with a Ouija board, like the possessed girl in *The Exorcist*. Bryson pointed out that Parker Brothers made the board, and they were based in Salem, Massachusetts, America's witchcraft headquarters. Likewise, Dungeons & Dragons started in Lake Geneva, Wisconsin, only eighteen miles from another Salem, no doubt a regional witchcraft hub.

I watched as four or five people at a time touched the pointer, not unlike Mormon priesthood holders laying hands on someone's head. They took turns asking questions, and the felt-bottomed pointer slid across the board. As the Ouija replied yes or no or spelled out answers, people laughed or made puzzled expressions. Whenever one of the Tremonton guys touched the pointer, it moved faster, so I assumed he was manipulating it. Matt and Janet asked about their future romantic prospects. Chad asked to speak with his sister who'd died in a car crash on the way to the Blue Mouse to see a German film. Maeve asked about her father and brother in England, and the cryptic answers made her mad.

Finally, I agreed to take a turn. "Tell me something no one else here would know," I said.

Without hesitation, the pointer spelled out B-A-T-H-R-O-O-M-F-L-O-O-R.

I felt a dark thrill go up my spine.

"It's stupid nonsense!" Maeve's eyes bulged with indignation. Sometimes she reminded me of the spoiled girl Veruca Salt in the *Willy Wonka* movie.

"I know what it's talking about," I said. "One time me and my girlfriend had sex on the bathroom floor."

Maeve glared, and the Tremonton guy gave me a self-satisfied smile.

On my next turn, I didn't want to trigger another eerily accurate reply, so I asked something safer. "Who's the most intelligent person in this room?"

I thought the answer might be me, but the Ouija board spelled out N-A-O-M-I. We all looked over at Naomi, sitting on her mattress across the room. She cocked her head and gave us a little wave, looking jaunty in the beret she always wore. Naomi was small and goblinish with a high-pitched voice, reminding me of the munchkin psychic lady in *Poltergeist*. Why would she be the most intelligent? Maybe because she wasn't playing with the Ouija board.

After a few more turns, Maeve suddenly grabbed the board and ran into the kitchen. Kneeling on the floor, she hunched over the board, her black leather jacket protecting her like a turtle's shell. With her hand on the pointer, she demanded information. When the pointer didn't move, she cursed the board and slammed it against the linoleum.

"It doesn't work with one person," whispered the Tremonton guy. We were watching Maeve from the hallway. Finally she let out a yell and threw the board like a Frisbee, denting a cupboard door.

That afternoon, we heard meowing from outside. Matt let in a strange-looking cat. Its face was flat with no snout, and its long, tawny fur was dirty and matted. While the cat ate tuna from a can, Janet picked at the knots in its fur. Later, Chad knelt beside the cat and blew pot smoke into its ears. Rather than mellowing out, the cat ricocheted around the room as if something were chasing it. We all agreed the Ouija board had somehow attracted the cat, so we named it Ouija.

Maeve wouldn't touch the Ouija board again. Some of us played a few more times, but we kept the sessions short and superficial. Whenever we played, the cat crouched under the kitchen table. We joked about using the board while frying, but no one did. By unspoken agreement, we never played after dark.

"Hey, where's that Ouija, anyway?" Matt asked one afternoon.

"Right here," Janet said. Ouija was sitting on her lap, purring as she brushed its long fur.

"The board, not the cat."

No one could find the board, and we never saw it again. I figured the game had somehow channeled our subconsciouses, but what was the scientific explanation?

At dusk one evening, my old Cabbage Patch roommate Virgil knocked on the Sub's door. One of the Tremonton girls tried to get him to come inside, but he just kept asking for me. Despite the cold, Virgil wasn't wearing a coat. He had on his usual preppie blue-striped Oxford shirt, khakis, and Bass Weejun loafers. He smiled at me, but I could tell he was uneasy. I couldn't imagine why he'd bothered to find me.

After stiffly greeting me, he said, "I wonder if I might reclaim my Beatles albums."

"Oh, yeah. Those are yours, aren't they." It had always surprised me how much Virgil loved the Beatles. Their music and Woody Allen movies were his only capitulations to modern pop culture. Otherwise, he pursued strictly classical music and literature.

I left Virgil on the porch and went into the living room. Slipping records into their sleeves, I noticed several were scratched. One Beatles cover had a cigarette burn on McCartney's face, and another was splattered with candle wax.

"Just tell him some punk stole them." Janet frowned at me as I gathered the albums. "That's what I told him while you were in California."

I gave her a look and didn't say anything. I didn't want to abuse Virgil any further.

With the albums under his arm, Virgil turned to leave, but then he turned back. "Would you like to come for a drive?"

I shrugged. "Sure."

As we puttered around the Avenues in the near dark, Virgil tried to tell me about his university studies, but we couldn't find our old dynamic. Whenever we made eye contact, he seemed to almost shudder. Part of me liked spooking him, but I wondered why he found me so creepy. I felt some guilt about our studio apartment, but I didn't see how the summer of 1984 could've been any different.

When Virgil mentioned prepping for his mission, I questioned myself for a moment. Had I made a mistake? Was that what I should've been doing too? But then I remembered Mormonism's white-daisy conformity and busywork, and I knew I never wanted to go back.

After Virgil dropped me off, I thought it'd be the last time I ever saw him.

With the Beatles gone, the Sub's vibe changed. More punks came around, some of them runaways drifting from punk house to punk house. I liked watching the punks—I felt like I were living in a forest where the wild animals trusted me. I liked the music they brought, like an anti-Reagan punk compilation called *Let Them Eat Jellybeans*. I didn't like leaving the Sub because I didn't want to miss anything. I wondered how the Sub compared to rival punk houses. We needed to start a band or zine or something.

Occasionally I pulled on the combat boots I'd stolen from Scott, the rankest of poseurs. Clomping around on the Sub's scuffed, dusty hardwood, I tried to feel more punk. But I knew I wasn't angry and macho enough—even Maeve was more macho than I was. Hardcore punks were shaven-headed monks of an extreme order, while I was a jumble of punk, new wave, psychedelia, and anything else cool that came my way. Deep down, I thought of punks as *them*, not *us*.

If I'd been born in the 1950s instead a few months before the Summer of Love, I thought maybe I would've made a good hippie. My personality was mellow. I loved the two main hippie drugs, pot and acid. But I didn't like how positive and caring the hippies were. All their talk of peace and love sounded like just another kind of church. I preferred new wave's decadent cynicism, laced with punk nihilism. Whenever Lisa or anyone started talking like a hippie, I turned sarcastic.

I encountered one intriguing mix of hippie and punk. The British band Crass was into anarchy but also peace. One day Lisa took us to a Crass apartment south of Trolley Square, the high-end shopping center where a teen Bosnian gunman would later kill five people. The intense Crass punks wore black militaristic clothes, and the Crass logo looked like a war machine. Some of Crass's slogans sounded hippie—"Fight war, not wars," "Destroy power, not people"—but they felt punk, with an angry, subversive edge.

Other punks called Crass punks "Crassholes." Compared to the Crass punks, I felt like a lightweight new waver. But I liked how Crass's music bounced and tickled in my brain, and I liked their doctrine that I shouldn't answer to any authority but myself. Crass made me think of Joseph Smith's only scripture I agreed with: "It is the nature and disposition of almost all men, as soon as they get a little authority, as they suppose, they will immediately begin to exercise unrighteous dominion."

If the Sub were becoming a real punk house, I knew it was because of Maeve. In the Salt Lake scene, the birthmark around her eye was a beacon of true punkness. Tina had traded sex for rent, but Maeve was trading her punk cred. When one punk who loved Maeve realized we were together, he wanted to beat me up, but Maeve stopped him.

Punks talked like they couldn't help being punk, like their spikes, chains, and mohawks sprouted from their DNA. As they talked about fighting with rockers, rednecks, and skinheads, sometimes they sounded like victims, other times like aggressors. Whenever punks sparred on the Sub's hardwood floor, Maeve would get in the middle of it, her black bangs whipping like a weapon, her harsh British laugh barking out. One punk told about Maeve defending him at a Black Flag gig. "The guy had me pinned on the ground. Before he could punch me, I saw a boot kick him in the head, and he rolled off. A hand reached down and pulled me up, and there was Maeve."

When punks tussled, I just watched, remembering my one attempt at fighting. Wanting to establish myself as a seventh-grade stud, one morning I'd dared a fat kid with a birth-defected arm to meet me after school under a certain tree. For the rest of the day, he punched me in the arm whenever we passed in the hallways. With his one overworked arm, his punches were surprisingly hard. When I punched him back, his fat barely even jiggled. After the last bell, I stayed in a second-floor classroom and watched out the window while the gimpy kid paced around the tree. The next day, people kept punching me and calling me a pussy, and I had to agree.

My hopes for the Sub rose when a wiry, dashing punk named Sean Fightmaster showed up. He was Salt Lake's best-known punk who wasn't in a band. He had a headful of spiky hair, and he wore skinheadish red suspenders, oxblood Doc Marten boots, and a jaunty plaid scarf. His parents were old hippies who encouraged him to rebel.

After his first visit, however, Fightmaster didn't come back to the Sub. I felt like we'd failed a test of authenticity. I later heard that, while fleeing from cops, Fightmaster ran through sprinklers with a hundred hits of acid in his pants pocket, and the acid soaked into his leg. When he got home, he tried to knife his mom because he thought she was a bull. After that, his brain was permafried. He eventually died from a drug overdose.

Another notorious Salt Lake punk was Big Shane, a tall, muscular, red-cheeked guy whose looks I envied. When his mohawk was spiked up, it reminded me of a dinosaur's skin sail running along its spine. When his mohawk hung limp, Big Shane wrapped his head with a red kerchief, making him look like a pirate. From the Sub's porch, he would shoot at passing cars with a powerful slingshot called a Wrist-Rocket, as if firing torpedoes from a submarine. When the police showed up at our door, part of me hoped they'd bust Big Shane, as I didn't see the point of damaging people's cars for no reason—that was chaotic evil, not chaotic neutral. But the cops just wanted to pick up a runaway named Miguel.

Late one frozen night, Big Shane showed up with a crowbar. Maeve and several other punks took off with him toward downtown Salt Lake. A few hours later, they returned with a bagful of coins from parking meters. Counting out the loot, they gave me a share toward Sub expenses, but I used it to eat several meals at the mall's food court. I could see some chaotic-neutral justification in taking what we needed, but the punks seemed too chaotic evil about it, reveling in the fun of breaking and stealing. Like Fightmaster, Big Shane would eventually die from drugs.

Part of me wanted to help steal things the Sub needed, but I didn't have the guts. The one time I'd shoplifted was at a toy store. After blowing my paper-route money on the pricey, hardcover *Dungeon Master's Guide*, I doubled back and tucked the two most expensive adventure modules, *Expedition to the Barrier Peaks* and *Tomb of Horrors,* behind my paper bag. Moseying out, I stopped near the cashier to admire polyhedral dice in a countertop display. It felt natural and easy to be chaotic neutral. I was stealing not to hurt the store but to fill a vital need.

When we played the modules, however, I wanted to brag about shoplifting them but felt too ashamed. I didn't consciously resolve not to shoplift again, but I never found the risk and uneasiness worth it. As a wannabe punk, I knew I should push myself to steal, but I felt relieved to keep letting the real punks do it. I hoped they'd soon find a way to pay for the Sub's rent and utilities.

Chapter 16

ONE AFTERNOON, WE ARRIVED HOME FROM CROSS-roads to find a middle-aged hippie with long hair and a walrus mustache sitting on our couch. I wanted to talk to the guy, but Matt kicked him out. He hated it when grownups tried to horn into our business, and the Sub's growing chaos was making him nervous. I could tell Lisa was feeling overwhelmed too, with too many people needing food, cigarettes, winter coats, and back rubs.

Some new wavers started bringing over their cocaine dealer. He wore a suit and tie like some kind of real-estate agent. I assumed he'd share, but he always took his paying customers into the bedroom and closed the door. I gave the dealer looks that said, *Dude, it's my house, so cut me in,* not knowing if I'd snort the coke or try to resell it. The dealer's response was to avoid eye contact. After he got people high, he would take off, leaving us to babysit his customers as they got freaky in the Sub.

I wondered if I could deal drugs instead of getting another low-paying cashier job. Supplying people with pot and LSD wouldn't even feel like work, as I'd usually do the drugs with them. Acid seemed easiest to sell, with tiny hits that police dogs probably couldn't sniff. But selling drugs could easily go wrong, like when I'd sold Bubble Yum in fifth grade. Before Bubble Yum, we'd chewed stiff pieces of Dubble Bubble or Bazooka. The new Bubble Yum gave instant pleasure, with soft, sugary flavor exploding in the mouth. It was so magical, Willy Wonka himself might have invented it. When the gum got scarce in Southern California. I asked my Seattle aunt to ship me down several packs. During recess, I chewed a piece in front of a cherubic Jewish kid.

"I'll buy a piece off you," he said.

"How much?"

He pulled out a quarter.

"For one piece?" Usually a quarter bought a whole pack.

"Indubitably." Mentally Gifted Minors used words like that.

I watched the Jewish guy unwrap the pink rectangle and set it on his tongue. As he began moving his jaws, he moaned and let his eyelids close.

At lunch, I sold my other pieces at five times their value. The next day, I brought two packs to school. Soon I requested a bigger shipment from Seattle. But then people started asking for credit and not paying me back. A rumor started that Bubble Yum's secret ingredient was spider eggs. A Jewish guy started singing me an Oompa-Loompa song about Miss Bigelow—that was the actual name Roald Dahl had used. When she couldn't find her gum, Miss Bigelow chewed up people's underwear and her boyfriend's nose. Finally, she chewed off her own tongue and was put in a sanatorium. Soon kids were calling me Miss Bigelow and making chewing noises in my ear.

During that time, I awoke one night with a bad stomachache. Running to the toilet, I heaved and heaved, but nothing came up. Finally, my stomach contorted in a strange way, and I felt something small and hard shoot out of my mouth. I hadn't turned on the light, so I couldn't see what it was. This happened eight more times, making me sweaty and sore. When I finally flipped on the light, I thought the toilet held nine pink grubs. Then I realized they were wads of Bubble Yum—the gum was so good I'd been swallowing it.

☯

One day I noticed a housefly buzzing around a thin, pale punk. At first, I didn't find this strange, but then I remembered it was frozen January outside. The fly should've been long dead.

I didn't think the punk noticed I was watching him, but suddenly he gave me a strange smile. He reminded me of Mel Gibson in *The Road Warrior,* my favorite movie since *Star Wars* and my first exposure to punk style. The punk's black leather jacket was scratched and torn, his clothes wrinkled and dusty. His choppy black hair looked more like bed head than punk style. Grainy black makeup bleared the skin under his eyes.

As I watched, the punk lifted his collar and let the fly crawl inside his shirt. Then he exited the Sub with some others, but he turned left where the others turned right. From the window, I watched the fly-punk walk up P Street, bobbing like a boat among piles of plowed snow. Just before he disappeared into the cemetery, he looked back and seemed to smile at me.

Some punks loved the nearby cemetery, Salt Lake's oldest and largest. At night, they'd roam the grounds searching for a certain Jewish crypt where you could light a candle, walk backward around the crypt three times, and then look inside and see a ghostly face with red eyes. Once, I heard a punk say something about catching a cat to kill in the cemetery—he might've been joking, but the Avenues were notorious for pet mutilations. I never joined a cemetery excursion, feeling no need to wander in the frozen darkness.

Over the next few days, I couldn't stop wondering about the fly-punk. I imagined him as lead singer of a Sub-based punk band called Lord of the Fly. As I thought about his preternatural fly, my mind kept returning to Dungeons & Dragons. Through a spell, a wizard could turn a creature into an intelligent familiar.

My favorite familiar had been a mouse—it was easy to keep hidden, and it made a good spy. My wizard could communicate telepathically with his mouse and see through its eyes. I could even cast certain spells through the mouse's tiny pink paws.

Had the fly-punk somehow tapped into real-life paranormality? I knew from *Omni* magazine that scientists had only just begun understanding our human brainpower. The preacher Lynn Bryson had told us about a Mormon kid named Jay who'd learned how to levitate small items, bend silverware, and ignite flames. That sounded like cool scientific brain discipline, but then Jay whacked out in unscientific directions, including gulping warm cow blood as it gushed out during satanic orgies. After Jay got baptized by immersion in blood, an evil spirit named Raul possessed him and drove him to kill himself—or so Bryson believed.

Jay sounded mentally unstable to me. I didn't believe in evil spirits. Any so-called occult power must have some not-yet-discovered scientific explanation. Bryson made it sound like the occult was common in Utah, with at least 10,000 witches and wizards living in the fifty miles between Nephi and Lehi, two towns named after Book of Mormon prophets. Attending high school within this ultra-Mormon zone, Jay and his girlfriend had found it easy to gather a coven of thirteen witches and warlocks.

Between classes at Bountiful High, sometimes I'd drawn occult symbols on chalkboards. Mostly I drew pentagrams but also the Egyptian ankh, druid symbols, and the hippie peace sign, which Bryson had said was Jesus Christ's cross turned upside down and broken. I made up Tolkienesque runes, as if writing secret messages. Occasionally I added the 666 logo from the antichrist movie *The Omen*. I signed my drawings "By-Tor," a character from early Rush songs who was sometimes good, sometimes evil. Despite my advertisements, however, no one invited me to join a coven.

Whenever the fly-punk returned to the Sub, Maeve went into the bedroom or hopped onto the Third Avenue bus downtown. I didn't talk to him much, but I always felt his strange, mesmerizing pull. If I wanted to go deeper and darker, all I had to do was ask the fly-punk. Somehow I knew it must be my own initiative, but the thought gave me thrills of nausea, so I kept putting it off.

In the afternoons after East High School let out, some kids started visiting the Sub, two punk boys and two new-wave girls who lived nearby in the Avenues. I wondered how they'd heard about us. Part of me liked wigging them out with our freakiness, but part of me didn't like having underage kids in the house.

When the two boys arrived one afternoon, several Subbers were tripping. Daytime tripping didn't feel as legit to me, like seeing a matinee instead of the evening show, but I'd joined them. I sat Indian-style on the hardwood floor, and the two impishly mohawked, combat-booted punks sat before me like disciples. Babbling psychedelically to them, I had little idea what I was saying, but I enjoyed watching their serious, fascinated expressions. I thought I was being funny, but they never once laughed. Sometimes they even gave each other astonished looks. Part of me liked playing the guru, but I also felt uneasy taking on a responsibility I wasn't sure I wanted.

The two girls were cute with their gel-spiked hair and Halloween-y makeup. Sometimes they brought us homemade soup, as if we were sick. Wanting to help us reconnect with the normal world, they talked Matt and me into going roller-skating out at the 49th Street Galleria. I'd loved roller-skating in sixth grade, but now I hated skating to pop music alongside smiling parents and children. I couldn't wait to get back aboard the Sub.

Then a smiley Hispanic girl from Salt Lake's west side showed up, looking only a little new wave. Over several days, she took each male down one at a time to the basement punk's bed. Both punk boys went down, Matt and Chad went down, and so did several others. Eric complained about his bed, but he had to admit it was punk. I couldn't imagine what the girl got out of it.

My turn came on Sunday morning, when most people were gone. I'd dreaded it, but I also wondered why my turn had come so late. In the basement bed, I tried kissing the girl, but she turned her face, wanting to connect only down below. We returned upstairs within five minutes. I felt discombobulated, as if a stranger had run past me and snatched my hat.

I wondered if Maeve would find out and if she'd care. The two of us were never alone together. Since our basement smoking game, we hadn't talked or touched romantically, beyond sleeping together somewhat cuddly in my boyhood bed. Recently she'd been favoring a bearish, frat-looking guy with bangs in his eyes.

When Lisa and Janet eventually realized what was happening with the Hispanic girl, they freaked out. One morning, Lisa tried to drive her home, but the girl took off on foot. We never saw her again.

"Maybe it's time to sink the Sub," Janet said that afternoon, laying on the couch in T-shirt and panties, holding a cigarette, and stroking Ouija. "It's out of control."

Folding his arms and shooting me a look, Matt nodded in agreement.

"We're overdue on bills anyway," Lisa said. Wearing a fuzzy green cardigan, she'd just come in from the kitchen, wiping her hands on a filthy dishtowel.

Not for the first time, I gave Lisa a pleading look, but she wouldn't make eye contact. She was still the only subhuman with a job. Deep down, I wanted to work again—not only did I need money, but I was tired of idleness. However, I always dressed punk for the mall, so no stores or restaurants would interview me. I considered it their problem, not mine.

Without income, I knew the Sub couldn't survive long, but I wanted to let things play out, not shut down prematurely. Maybe it would take the landlord several months to evict us. If the electricity shut off, the shoplifters could get us batteries and candles. We needed the furnace and hot water, but natural gas was cheap—we could cover it with coins from panhandling and parking meters, if nothing else.

On the other hand, the Sub was starting to wear me out. I showered most days, but no one cleaned the bathroom. Over Christmas I'd washed my socks and underwear, but now I was reusing dirty pairs, not always sure they belonged to me. No one laundered the communal clothes or the bedding. Our dishes usually sat dirty in the sink and on the counters. Lisa or Matt took out the garbage every so often, but no one swept the floors. We'd started burning incense to mask the funk. When I heard the Adolescents song "Kids of the Black Hole," I realized it perfectly described punk houses like the Sub.

Part of me felt totally free in the Sub, but part of me felt stuck, endlessly waiting to see who came over to entertain, intoxicate, or feed us. Lately we'd noticed a patrol car parked across the street for hours at a time. This upset some people, but I liked having cops nearby, in case the Sub's chaos went too far. My only bustable activity was drugs, but I only partook of them, never possessed them. One punk claimed the TV news had run a story on Salt Lake punk houses and flashed the Sub onscreen as one of several examples. This got me fantasizing about how much more infamous the Sub could become, if only we could stay afloat.

Despite my objections, Lisa, Janet, and Matt moved ahead with scuttling the Sub. As soon as Maeve realized what was happening, she broke off any pretense of our relationship. "I'm unsure about your sexuality," she informed me. I knew I was hetero, but I couldn't blame her. Half the Sub was gay or lesbian, and I'd never made another move on her, after my one failed try.

The basement punk's dad came over to pick up his bed. He was a typical white-bread Mormon, his face and belly bloated with sugar-fat, his military-short hair parted on the right. He wore thick-framed eyeglasses, polyester slacks, and a white dress shirt that showed his temple undergarment's smile-shaped neckline.

"Things getting too heavy around here, huh?" the dad asked me.

"Yeah, too much traffic."

"The police are just doing their job." He gave me a smug look. I'd meant too many freaks were coming over, not the police. I realized the basement punk's dad must've called the cops to watch us. Years later, his son would wander onto a busy highway in the dark and get hit by two cars.

When I unpacked in Bountiful, my assortment of clothes was different than when I'd left. My parents seemed relieved to have me home but also resigned. My dad wanted to contact the U and see about reinstating my Honors at Entrance scholarship. But I just wanted to get some income flowing and rent my next apartment, so I could keep exploring the underground. At the Sub, I'd failed to overcome my jitters about several chaotic-neutral opportunities—connecting with the fly-punk, finding my own wholesale LSD source, developing my petty-theft skills, devirginizing Maeve—but I hoped I'd get more chances soon.

Chapter 17

MATT GOT A JOB AT A PIZZA PLACE UNDER THE ZCMI mall's easternmost escalators, over in the ultra-Mormon zone. Sitting at a table with a Coke, I watched him serve customers and wipe counters, always staying in motion. The owner, a Middle Eastern woman, obviously liked him. I wondered why he hadn't gotten the job when the Sub needed it.

The Sub had seemed to last a long time, but it wasn't even two full months, less than the Cabbage Patch or Dana Point. We'd tried doing it Matt's way in California and my way in the Avenues, but neither had worked. Without the Sub, our group had shrunk back to just Matt, Lisa, Janet, Vince, Chad, and me. Now our only hangouts were the downtown malls, the Maxim, and places like Ben's Café and the Salt Lake Roasting Company.

"You better get a job soon," Matt warned me. "Or I might get a place without you. I refuse to live at home."

I was trying. Instead of punkishly wandering around the malls, now I looked for jobs in the newspaper. When I applied for jobs, I flattened my hair, took out my earring, and dressed normal. I even tried selling newspaper subscriptions door to door, but I hated bugging people and it didn't pay enough. I got some interviews, but I couldn't close the deal with anyone.

Before long, Matt brought a new guy into our circle. Lance was a downtown scenester who'd lived in several punk houses, but he wasn't punk at all. He wore Guess jeans and shopped at trendy boutiques in Trolley Square. He didn't have a car, but he made money bussing tables at a downtown restaurant and dating middle-aged men.

I envied Lance's tallness, strong jawline, and dark, wavy hair with highlights. His eyes always stayed icy blue, while mine waffled between blue, green, and gray, depending on what I was wearing. Lance wasn't effeminate, but he flamed in a goofy, boyish way. When he laughed, he put his whole face into it, his chin stretching down like Herman Munster's on the old black-and-white TV show.

Lance liked the poppy, synthesized type of new wave. He called the Maxim "the disco," which bugged me. When he danced, he threw around his arms like a big gorilla. One time, he lip-synched Depeche Mode's "Shake the Disease" onstage at the Maxim. Near the end of the song, he shattered a glass orb the size of a cantaloupe. The Maxim had to stop the music, turn on the lights, and send someone out with a Shop-Vac. Little did we know this act was a premonition of things to come.

When Matt could see I wasn't getting a job, he rented a small apartment with Lance in a sleazy building on Fourth East, next to a drycleaner called the Red Hanger, which we joked was an abortion clinic. The bedroom barely fit their two mattresses. In the front room, the only furniture was Matt's grandma's green couch, still redolent of the Sub. For the next several weeks, I slept on the couch most nights.

I hated being the visitor instead of the host. Late one night, I arrived downtown on the last bus and couldn't wake up Matt or Lance, so I had to sleep in their stairwell. Another time, I left my parents' Mazda parked nearby while we went on a three-day drug binge. When I recovered enough to drive home, I couldn't find the car.

"It got stolen," I told my dad from a payphone.

"Not this time," he said. Our motorhome had previously been stolen downtown. "We came and found it. Your brother needed it." He paused. "Please don't do that again. And no more smoking in the car."

The next weekend, my parents took me to see *The Falcon and the Snowman,* about a CIA employee from our Palos Verdes neighborhood who'd got caught selling secrets to the Russians. "At least I'm not that bad," I said during ice cream after the movie. My parents smiled, but not convincingly.

With Maeve gone, Tina came back, as I'd hoped and dreaded she would. I'd learned to go hours without thinking about her, if not yet whole days, but now this progress was undone. In contrast with Maeve's gray, defensive pill bug, Tina was a pretty, flitting ladybug. As we sat in Matt and Lance's dingy front room, her playful eyes and high-pitched giggle penetrated me. Drawing nearer, I caught whiffs of her lemongrass-scented shampoo, so fresh and clean despite any recent sluttiness. Tina gave me complicated looks of encouragement tinged with cringing apology.

When the apartment got dark and quiet, Tina and I entwined on the green couch, hoping we didn't wake Janet. Afterward, I wondered what it meant. Were we now a couple again? Had we ever been a couple in the first place? The next night, I broke Chad's other acid rule and got intimate with Tina while frying. At first it felt extra-cool, but then I started feeling slivers of slimy flesh on my fingertips, as if Tina were falling apart inside.

That weekend, Janet's friend visited from Clearfield. "She's coming down to get laid," Janet told me. "Vince is gonna do the honors." I wondered how Janet really felt about this, since we all knew she liked Vince. The friend was a rocker chick, not new wave or punk. In the middle of the night, she and Vince coupled only a few feet away from where I lay on green couch. The next evening, the rocker chick sat next to me and whispered, "We should do it too." I made a laughish sound and looked away. Not only was I unsure of my Tina status, but the rocker chick's offer embarrassed me and grossed me out.

A new-wave girl named Jen sometimes came around Matt and Lance's place. One evening, Jen talked us into driving out to her parents' house in ultra-Mormon West Jordan. The place disgusted me with its pastel carpet and furniture, homemade crafts, pictures of temples and scripture scenes, and nauseatingly wholesome-smelling potpourri. Jen's mom set out brownies, lemon squares, rice crispy treats, root beer, and Sprite. She tried to smile at us, but I could tell she was confused and worried.

"Get us out of here," I whispered to Lisa. As we left, I smirked at the mother. *Jen chose us over you.*

Lance's friend Travis was more flamboyant and effeminate than Lance, but I liked him better. Looking and acting like a dark-haired David Bowie, he was always saying bizarre, random things in a theatrical way. He loved weed, wine, and acid. When he brought over some drawings and paintings he'd done, I recognized real creative talent.

Travis lived with his parents out in the Salt Lake Valley's southwest corner, which had even more rednecks and polygamists than Bountiful did. Neither of us had a job, but I suggested we find an apartment together. I wasn't worried about Travis's gayness—I knew he knew I wasn't gay. We wanted a cooler location than Matt and Lance's, so we looked on Capitol Hill, right above downtown Salt Lake. Between two mansions on Second North, we found a red-tile-roofed bungalow with two

bedrooms, a living room, a dining room, and a big sunlit studio.
The bungalow was a block up from LDS worldwide headquarters
and a block down from the Utah State Capitol.

Travis and I asked our dads for money, but we both got refused.
I wasn't willing to let the place go, so I asked Matt and Lance to
rent it with me. When Lance saw the bungalow, he freaked out.
But then he started moping. "It's probably—what, six or seven
hundred a month?"

"No. Three-sixty."

Lance whooped like a high-school jock. With rent split three
ways, it would cost them each less than their crummy place did.
"I even like this red carpet," he said.

"I love all the windows," Matt said. "It's the perfect summer
apartment." He gave me a serious look. "But what about a job?"

Lance walked me straight down to the restaurant where he
worked, two blocks from the bungalow. Located atop a twenty-
five-story tower, Nino's was a swank Italian place with spectacu-
lar views of the valley and surrounding mountains. The manager
hired me as a valet, and the three of us rented the bungalow. I
loved being back in my own apartment and finally having my
own bedroom. Janet got the green couch all to herself again. Her
long hair soon clogged the tub drain, so we had to shower standing in a foot of slimy gray water.

Along with my childhood bed and dresser, I furnished my bedroom
with an end table, a director's chair, and a yellow-painted desk that
had belonged to my sisters. On the wall, I hung two of my kinder-
garten crayon drawings, titled "A Dinosaur Left in the Rain" and
"A Space Crab Juggling a Space Monster." Staring at them from my
bed, I wondered how I could become that creative again.

We signed up for home-delivered milk, bread, eggs, butter, and cheese. For our housewarming party, Lance borrowed elegant plates, serving dishes, glasses, and silverware from Nino's, and he stole champagne and caviar. On the night of the party, he greased back his hair like Clark Gable and put on a blue silk smoking jacket he'd found at Grunts & Postures. Below the waist, however, he wore his usual Guess denim shorts and boat shoes without socks.

Soon the apartment was full of high-energy gays, along with a few fashionable lesbians. They crowded the red-carpeted living and dining rooms and danced in Lance's hardwood-floored studio. Puffing from a silver cigarette holder, Lance moved from room to room, sharing his cartoonish laugh and glacier-blue eyes. Something about the setup reminded me of Poe's story "The Masque of the Red Death," with AIDS as the pestilence stalking us. After the second chicken-hawkish guy hit on me, I got Lisa to take me to a movie.

I tried to like Lance, but I kept wishing I didn't live with him. I found him smug in his gayness and too cynical about everything else, including punk. He pulled Matt in an annoyingly yuppy direction. The bungalow was cool, but it didn't have the Sub's underground potential. What was I going to do with my life?

Chapter 18

LIVING SO CLOSE TO MORMON HEADQUARTERS FELT like escaping Catholicism by moving into the Vatican's shadow. We called the gray, gothic temple Sleeping Beauty's Castle. We mocked the tall, white, phallic Church Office Building with its two massive globes at the base. I'd been inside the tower once, to visit my uncle who worked as a church historian. I'd entered the temple a couple times, but only the basement to perform baptisms for the dead, which had been disappointingly nonghoulish.

When it was wet or cold outside, runaway punks took shelter in Temple Square's visitor centers or the massive domed tabernacle. I'd heard of punks and new wavers touring Temple Square while high, giggling through presentations, asking ridiculously cosmic questions, and tripping out on the creepy Disney-style animatronics. I didn't feel any desire to hang out in Temple Square. When I walked through, I was just taking a shortcut like any other worldly pedestrian. Occasionally I fantasized about spray-painting underground symbols, especially punk's occult-looking red A for anarchy. But mostly I gave no thought to the church as I passed through its heart.

As the weather warmed, we took nighttime fry walks around downtown and the lower Avenues. In residential areas, dogs barked at us with unusual hostility, as if they could sense our abnormal psychedelic wavelength. As we passed the Cosmic Aeroplane bookstore one night, a pickup truck pulled over, three cowboys jumped out, and one of them punched Lance in the face. Then they jumped back in and took off, squealing their tires.

"It's OK." Lance rubbed his cheek. "It doesn't matter."

I felt shocked but also glad they'd targeted Lance, rather than anyone else. Letting out a sob, Lisa hugged him. She'd been crying more lately, and for some reason she was still wearing sweaters, even though it was warm.

During our fry walks, we avoided a certain hotel two blocks south of Temple Square. In 1978, soon after my family moved to Utah, a cult-brainwashed mother and her seven children had jumped from the hotel's eleventh floor. One of our Bigelow cousins belonged to the family's cult, and now she helped care for a daughter who'd survived with major disabilities. I'd never had a bad acid trip, and I didn't want the hotel to trigger one.

One moonlit night, we headed to Memory Grove while frying. Near the park's entrance, Matt pointed out a punk house. "I heard they do heroin in there," he said. I couldn't tell if he was warning me, goading me, or both. As I stared, the house started bouncing in place, each window pulsing with a different neon color. I felt a strong urge—almost an inner command—to find out what was happening inside the house. But as we walked past, Lisa grabbed my arm, as if to restrain me.

Wedged in a narrow canyon between Capitol Hill and the Avenues, Memory Grove featured several war memorials. As we entered, Lisa shone her flashlight on a pentagram embedded in the rock-paved walkway. She told us the park's monuments were all laid out in a giant pentagram pattern. I'd thought pentagrams were exclusively satanic, but the downtown Mormon temple was

carved with some, and I knew Mormonism couldn't be satanic—
it was too wholesome, pure, and boring. What would've been
cool was if Mormons could use pentagrams to summon angels
instead of demons. Maybe then I could've put up with the white-
shirt conformity and busywork.

We wandered across the silvery lawn. The trees gyrated like
monsters, and I kept watching to make sure they stayed rooted
in place. Built of marble and granite, the monuments looked
like pagan altars or miniature Greek temples. In the moonlight,
City Creek flowed like raw mercury through the park. The acid-
enhanced sounds of water and wind made me wish the ocean
were nearby, instead of a shallow, salty, stinky lake.

As we sat and smoked on one monument, I told a story some
Kimball cousins had told me. Late one night, a couple was
driving too fast on the canyon road above the Grove. The boy
lost control, and the car plunged down into the park. The cops
found his body, but all they found of the girl was one of her legs.
Sometime later, another couple pulled over on the canyon road,
looking for the mysterious spot where cars rolled backward up
the hill. Suddenly a ghoulish woman hopped on one leg toward
them. As the boy peeled out, the Hoppy Lady jumped on the
car's roof, ripped it open, and pulled out the girl. When the cops
found the girl's body, her leg was missing.

"I have a real story for you," Travis said. "It happened to me, not
someone else." One summer night, he'd gone to a party at Hot
Toddy's house in the upper Avenues. Drinking too much, he passed
out. Early the next morning, he woke up cold and naked in Memory Grove, lying on a monument with his clothes scattered nearby.

"Which monument?" I asked.

Travis pointed across the lawn. "That one—I don't want to
go near it. But hold on, the story's not over. When I got home,
I went to take a shower. In the mirror, I saw three little pricks,
right here." He touched himself above his collarbone.

"Isn't that where your jugular is?" I asked.

"Maybe it was a three-fanged vampire," Matt said.

"I think it was devil worshippers," Travis said. "They took some of my blood."

"I'm sorry, babe." Lisa scooted closer to side-hug Travis. She sounded concerned but also amused. All evening she'd been pretending to fry, but I'd seen her flick away her nugget of purple gel like a booger.

Where the mown grass stopped at the end of Memory Grove, we crossed the road and continued up into City Creek Canyon, following Lisa's flashlight through scrub oak and maple shrubs.

"Hey," a male voice called out ahead.

"Hi," I heard Lisa say. She sounded surprised but not alarmed.

When we caught up, Lisa was standing with a young guy in the crumbling foundation of an old pioneer cabin. A small fire guttered in one corner. The guy wore a cowboy hat and boots.

"What're you doing out here, Buck?" Lisa asked.

He pointed up the canyon. "The devil worshippers took my girlfriend."

Looking up the canyon, I thought I saw an orange blip that could've been a bonfire. My ears caught noise on the breeze like distant yelling, but I couldn't be sure on acid.

"That's horrible," Lisa said.

"I could use some help." Buck looked at Lance, the biggest of us. "We gotta get her back."

"Sorry, man." Lance's voice sounded strangely macho. "We're all frying on acid right now."

Just then, I noticed a rifle propped in another corner of the foundation.

"You better be careful," Buck said. "They're always looking for girls." He suddenly turned to Janet. "Like *you*."

Janet yelped and stepped back.

"We better go," Matt said. "*Now*."

As we walked back through Memory Grove, Travis asked, "Did that really just happen?"

After my LSD trip ended, I still wondered about Buck. From a young age, I'd heard rumors of devil worshippers in City Creek Canyon. According to the traveling preacher Lynn Bryson, devil worship was real. If we played the Eagles song "Hotel California" backward, we could hear a voice say, "Satan organized his own religion." The hotel on the album cover was the real-life headquarters of the Church of Satan.

If Buck were trying to rescue his girlfriend, why was he just sitting by a fire? He seemed more like some kind of sentinel. I wondered what would've happened if we'd followed him further up the canyon. I didn't think devil worship was real, but maybe one of the occult sciences used human blood as a chemical activator, and Buck's group needed fresh donors.

Leaving our bungalow one day, I crossed the street to try a shortcut between two apartment buildings. In the middle of the block, I found a small, fenced, grassy area that contained a monument. I realized I'd been here before—it was the gravesite of my great-great-great-grandfather Heber C. Kimball.

I lit a cigarette and skimmed the plaque. Seven of Heber's wives were buried with him, including my great-great-great-grandmother Vilate, Heber's first and real wife, not one of the forty-something wives who came after. Like my mom eventually would, Vilate had ten children. Also buried here were eighteen of Heber's sixty-six children.

I realized our bungalow must be located on Heber's original homestead. As second-in-command to Brigham Young, Heber had claimed the block kitty-corner to Temple Square, plus additional lands. Before the state capitol was built, the whole

south-facing hillside had been called Heber's Bench. Up near
Park City, Kimball Junction and Heber City were named after
him too. In Bountiful, the ruins of Heber's gristmill lay across
the street from my high school. The men had harnessed wild
bears to turn the mill.

As a kid, I'd heard freaky stories about Heber and Vilate. At
one point, Joseph Smith asked Heber to give up Vilate so Joseph
could marry her. For three days, Heber fasted, prayed, and wept.
When he brought Vilate to Joseph, Joseph congratulated him for
passing an Abrahamic test of sacrifice. Then he sealed Heber and
Vilate as a couple for eternity.

However, the test wasn't over yet. Joseph told Heber he
needed to start practicing polygamy himself. Heber offered to
marry two old-maid sisters who were friends with Vilate. "That
arrangement is of the devil," Joseph said. "You go and get you a
young wife, one you can take to your bosom and love and raise
children by."

Joseph chose a young Englishwoman for Heber to marry
without Vilate's knowledge. Heber begged Joseph to reconsider,
but Joseph said it was the Lord's commandment—if Heber
didn't take this second wife, he would lose his apostleship and be
damned. Heber married the woman, but it made him miserable.
Vilate couldn't get him to confess what was wrong, so she prayed.
She saw a vision that explained polygamy as the key to eternal
power, glory, and exaltation. She gave Heber the OK.

But the test still wasn't over. Joseph Smith decided to take
Heber and Vilate's fourteen-year-old daughter as his plural wife.
Heber saw the match as a way to join his family with the prophet's, but Vilate found it almost as hard as sharing Heber with
another wife. After the secret sealing ceremony, the daughter
remained with her parents. A year later, Joseph was martyred.

Once the church moved to Utah and went public with polygamy, Heber became one of its biggest promoters. He claimed a

man with one wife "soon begins to wither and dry up," but a man with many wives "looks fresh, young, and sprightly." Marrying just one extra wife was wimpy—a real man needed lots of wives.

I tossed my cigarette butt into the monument's damp flower-bed, half-jokingly wondering if Heber and Vilate's ghosts could sense my non-Mormonness. They were already used to descendants disappointing them, as most of Heber's forty-four sons had gone feral after he died. Kimballs seemed to have a rambunctious side, and maybe I'd inherited some of that. Part of me wished I could be a sexually radical stud like Heber, but I couldn't imagine how so-called prophets and apostles could justify copulating with multiple women, whether in Old Testament times or early Mormonism. Even as a worldly, carnal apostate, I wanted only Tina. But I'd just broken up with her again because Chad told me she was sleeping with someone else.

Chapter 19

T HE UNIVERSITY OF UTAH REINSTATED MY HONORS AT
Entrance scholarship for spring quarter of 1985. At my dad's
urging, I decided to try majoring in business, wondering how
my brain would function after my druggy year off. But I considered my real school to be Cosmic Aeroplane, the counterculture
wonderland four blocks down the hill from our house. Smelling
of incense and patchouli, Cosmic was Salt Lake's hub for everything alternative, including books, magazines, music, New Age
crystals, tarot cards, freaky clothes and jewelry, and of course the
basement headshop. Cosmic even stocked a full range of Mormon books, from apostolic to apostate. It lacked only an adjoin-
ing coffeehouse or café.

At first, I'd felt intimidated by Cosmic's headshop, worried
I'd be obvious as a neophyte, clueless about the secret words and
gestures. After a few visits, however, I felt as comfortable down
there as I did buying cigarettes at 7-Eleven. My first headshop
purchase was a purple-and-magenta tie-dyed T-shirt and matching rolling papers. However, the smoke tasted inky, and I got
mocked for the psychedelic color coordination. Eventually I
splurged on a purple water pipe, as Utah law required Cosmic
to call bongs.

Upstairs, I browsed the occult books, wondering which para-
normal science might hold the key to my future. But I realized
what I really wanted was to escape back into fiction. For some

reason, I'd stopped reading when I moved into the Cabbage Patch. Wandering through Cosmic, I couldn't get interested in my old genres of mystery, fantasy, and sci-fi, but the horror section drew me. I felt hungry for some modern-day supernatural. I'd never tried Stephen King, so I read *The Shining* and then binged through *Carrie, 'Salem's Lot, Night Shift, The Dead Zone, Firestarter, Cujo, Different Seasons, Christine, Pet Sematary, Thinner,* and *Skeleton Crew.* When the time was right, I would read King's thickest book, the postapocalyptic *The Stand.*

Even more than books, I loved Cosmic's underground periodicals. I'd stand and read weird magazines until my legs hurt. Whenever I could afford it, I bought issues and stacked them on my bedroom end table, so people could sit in my director's chair and browse. I'd done the same as a kid, keeping piles of *Mad, Dragon, Omni,* and *Rolling Stone* for my friends.

I liked following the punk scene via two West Coast zines, *Flipside* and *Maximum Rocknroll.* Punk seemed full of rebellions within rebellions. I didn't understand how skinheads could take Nazism seriously. I didn't get how straightedge punks could rebel against sex and drugs—it made as much sense as acting Mormon while drinking, smoking, and fornicating. The L.A. scene was full of fighting between punks and the police, gangs, and even other punks. The Salt Lake scene was mellower, more unified, and deeper underground. I wanted to dive back in.

In a magazine called *The Match,* I learned about anarchy and atheism. As far as I could tell, the only real theological choice was between Mormonism, satanism, and atheism—everything else was half-assed. Another magazine I liked was the pot porn of *High Times,* with its centerfolds of brightly lit, Venusian-looking plants oozing with sap. My favorite magazine was *Processed*

World out of San Francisco, an artsy, satirical rebellion against corporations and consumerism. As I read about fascist corporations controlling everything and squashing creativity and dissent, I realized why the LDS church was so lame. The Utah corporate headquarters had formulated a bland, lowbrow, one-size-fits-all Mormon product. If religions were restaurants, Mormonism would have been McDonald's.

One afternoon while browsing through gaming magazines, I came across a dusty, shelf-worn copy of *The Oracle,* the third of the five issues I'd published during high school. Only about three years had passed since I'd published my Dungeons & Dragons magazine, but the copy seemed like an artifact from my distant childhood. I loved the cover illustration, a massive snake with the head of a crocodile. The Compleat Strategist in Manhattan had carried *The Oracle,* so New York writers and artists had started sending me submissions. One later co-created the Teenage Mutant Ninja Turtles, and another worked on a parody called Adolescent Radioactive Blackbelt Hamsters.

As I flipped through the *Oracle* pages, I remembered feeling proud of the issue's adult realism. I'd considered hiding it from my parents, but I published out of my dad's basement office, so that wasn't possible. Soon enough, they'd called me upstairs to their master bedroom.

"First of all," my dad began, "are this woman's breasts bare?" On the back cover, a fantasy comic showed a woman with unclothed breasts, but the artist had left off her nipples.

"No, definitely not," I said. I felt glad he hadn't noticed the possible glimpse of the woman's bush.

"What we're really concerned about," my dad continued, "is this." He flipped to an article titled "The Courtesan: A New Character Class for AD&D," which described how male or female players could roleplay a female character initially as a virgin and advance her to wench, tart, whore, harlot, and madam.

"Did you write this?" my mom asked. My parents knew I used pseudonyms—on the masthead, I listed five imaginary staff members.

"No, a guy in the military did."

"That makes more sense," my dad said.

"These people aren't Mormon," I explained to my mom.

"Yes, but you are."

Oh, really? I thought. *We shall see.*

By that time, I wasn't playing D&D much anymore—the magazine itself had become my game. Part of me wished the military guy had taken his article even further. If we could use dice to determine combat blow by blow, why not sex? But all he wrote was, "If referees don't want to play out ordinary encounters, presume characters earn 25 gold pieces per week." I also wished he'd included a male character version. Schoolmates often sang me "Just a Gigolo" with my surname in place of *gigolo*.

Standing in Cosmic, I realized *The Oracle* was the coolest thing I'd ever done. Unlike other amateur D&D magazines I'd seen, *The Oracle* was impressive enough that adult gaming professionals sent me editorials against D&D's grand wizard Gary Gygax, who'd turned into a greedy corporate control freak. I'd loved publishing dissent and feeling part of the underground gaming resistance.

Why couldn't I do something like *The Oracle* again? Instead of half-assing college, maybe I could publish a magazine about the alternative scene, covering punk and other trippy counter-cultural stuff. Maybe I could become the oracle of the Salt Lake underground.

Several weeks after our last breakup, Tina finally showed up at the bungalow again. Crinkling her eyes, she spouted wacky banter, her voice even higher and gigglier than I'd remembered. When our eyes met, Tina didn't cringe anymore. After the reunion died down, she came over to me. She'd upgraded her clothes and makeup. Her front teeth were pure white, with no bulimic stains. She made me feel buzzy, like breaking my nicotine fast with the day's first cigarette.

"You've got to try this." Tina reached into her oversized handbag and pulled out a Styrofoam carton. Inside were lumps of what looked like glistening Play-doh.

"What is it?" I asked.

"Sushi!" She popped a piece in her mouth. "Mmm."

"What's sushi?" I asked.

"Oh, it's just . . . *raw fish!*" She tried to put a piece in my mouth, but I turned away. "Did you turn into Gollum?" I asked. She gave me a confused look.

In my bedroom, Tina sat on my bed and pulled a black leather portfolio from her bag. "Guess what. I'm a model now!"

Leafing through her portfolio, I couldn't believe how sexy she looked. She'd recently appeared in several newspaper ads for Zion's Cooperative Mercantile Institution. Though founded by Brigham Young and still church-owned, ZCMI apparently didn't screen its models for moral purity. She also had some artsy photos. In one, she was naked except for white frosting swirled around her body, like a human cinnamon roll. My gut churned. How many people had she slept with since I'd last seen her?

Later, Tina took my hand and walked me up State Street to her new top-floor apartment across from the state capitol. She shared it with a spacy, anorexic model whose extra-short bangs made her look mentally challenged. Tina's room was more of a sun porch than a real bedroom, with lots of curtainless windows. She had a double bed with soft, clean, fragrant, white bedding.

"You guys just need to stay together," Janet advised me when I arrived home the next morning.

"That's what I want," I said. I felt paranoid about Tina's photographer, who she'd mentioned several times. But I also wondered if, with all her recent improvements, things might be different now.

Over the next several weeks, I enjoyed sleeping in Tina's love nest, except when the sunlight woke us early, which Tina liked. On evenings when I valeted late, I slept in my own bed and feared Tina wasn't alone in hers. I wanted to ask her for an exclusive commitment, but I didn't want to ruin our good vibe and I didn't think she could ever keep it.

Tina admitted she still puked every day, but she wasn't doing the stomach-stretching binges anymore, and she used laxatives only before a fashion show or swimsuit shoot. Down at the studio, they gave her too much cocaine. She also wanted to cut down on cigarettes. But she worried if she smoked or snorted less, she would eat more.

One afternoon, I took a bus down West Temple to Tina's studio. The shoot wasn't finished yet, so she invited me to watch. After a woman refreshed her makeup, the photographer held white powder to her nostrils, like some kind of internal cosmetic. When the drug kicked in, Tina stared at her photographer with the same mesmerized, adoring expression she'd given the cocaine cowboy at the Cabbage Patch. Between poses, the photographer walked over and touched her. When he gave me a gloating smile, I knew for sure.

"Are we playing head games again?" Tina asked a few days later. "Is that it?"

I knew I was Tina's favorite—why wasn't that enough? But I couldn't help withdrawing from her again, and we both knew we'd completed another cycle. I stopped hiking up to her love nest, and she came over to socialize less often. I returned to my misery of hoping another beautiful, charming nymphomaniac would seduce me and then stay faithful to me.

Chapter 20

WHEN LISA INTRODUCED US TO A LESBIAN NAMED Lucy, we sensed tension between the two. Lisa pursued Lucy, but Lucy was skittish in return, sometimes even ornery. However, Lucy loved our Capitol Hill group. With her nonstop zany energy, she brought a new Tigger dynamic to the bungalow, while Lisa kept getting more neurotic, like Rabbit.

Lucy had warm brown eyes and kinky, shoulder-length hair. I envied her intelligence and functionality, as she held a cushy office job, had her own apartment and car, and studied at the U. Lucy wasn't much into punk or new wave, but she took copious drugs and even sold some. However, she saw no point in tobacco. "Go ahead, smoke like a chimney!" she'd sometimes cry when we lit cigarettes. I knew she was right—I enjoyed nicotine buzzes upon waking and after meals, but otherwise my constant smoking just burned money and lung cells.

Lucy's main pot source was a young, unsmiling teen she called Rocker Don because of his long, greasy hair and AC/DC and Iron Maiden T-shirts. He lived in a rundown house near Liberty Park, a neighborhood my mom had warned us to avoid. To buy pot from Rocker Don, Lucy drove into an alley almost hidden by overgrowth and parked in a junk-strewn, bare-dirt area, where we waited for Rocker Don to come out. One rainy day, Lucy's tires spun in the mud and Rocker Don had to push us out.

We entered Rocker Don's house only once, to smoke ganja with him late one evening. His place had rough, raw-wood floors and almost no furniture. As we were leaving, Rocker Don's mother arrived home. With long black hair, glowing pale skin, and heavily mascaraed eyes, she radiated Elvira witchery. It was like meeting the monster Grendel's mother—luckily, we hadn't done anything to harm her son.

For some reason, I took the lead in chatting with Rocker Don's mom. Everything came out in a sarcastic flirting tone, and she answered in similar mode. I felt eerily drawn to the woman. If I wanted to get into something deeper, some kind of black magic, I sensed Rocker Don's mom could take me there. I knew I was still only up to my hips in the Salt Lake underground.

One afternoon, Lucy took us to the house where local punk band L.D.S. lived. They let us squeeze onto their shabby couches and smoke their hash, but they sneered at us. The name L.D.S. supposedly stood for Local Death Squad, but their flyers sometimes said, "It doesn't mean a thing," obviously referring to the religion. In their shows, L.D.S. used smoke, candelabras, and corpse makeup. For their album cover, they'd posed in the cemetery near the Sub. I wanted to make friends with a punk band, but these guys seemed too hokey and yet also intimidating. Like Black Flag, they were better at attitude than music.

Near Trolley Square, Lucy showed us a freaky secret garden called Gilgal. "You have to be sober your first time," she said, "or you won't believe it." In a backyard behind a fragrant Wonder Bread factory, an eccentric Mormon bishop had created dozens of rock sculptures with religious and Masonic themes. My favorite was a car-sized sphinx carved with the face of Joseph Smith. When we returned to fry in the moonlight, I stared at the sphinx for what felt like hours, daring it to speak me a mystery. The prophet's stone face kept transmogrifying, but I didn't hear any voices.

☯

At the U, I saw a flyer for a weeklong summer program in Park City called Writers at Work. I registered for the creative-nonfiction track, hoping I could start developing some kind of magazine for Salt Lake's alternative scene. Trying to write about punk, I complained how emotionally limited the rebellion was. *The anger, frustration, and hopelessness we feel about an impersonal, uninspiring industrial society cannot be changed by allowing these emotions to totally dominate us. Maybe we should try to combine the aggression of punk with the peaceful means of the hippies.* The teacher gave me a B+.

After the writing workshop, I started visiting Bountiful more often so I could use my dad's word processor. I didn't want to do a punk fanzine with band interviews and album reviews—Salt Lake already had enough of those. I wanted to go wider and deeper in the Salt Lake underground. I wanted my magazine to somehow capture the whole Cosmic Aeroplane scene, not just punk.

Growing up, I'd heard prophecies that Salt Lake would become the world's "wickedest" city. Now I wanted Salt Lake to become the world's coolest, most radical city in some new way no other city could match. I wanted Salt Lake to break out of its vanilla Mormon shell, but I didn't want us to become a clone of Los Angeles. *Let the rest of the nation follow us,* I wrote, but I also wrote some yuppie-sounding stuff about new restaurants, shopping, and skyscrapers.

While high one evening, I remembered how the Mormon pioneers had made the Utah desert "blossom as the rose." A magazine name came to me: *Flourishing Wasteland.* Photocopied on green paper, the first issue was solid text. *This fanzine is admittedly small and unadorned,* I wrote, *and might lack any degree of directed purpose in content. But we will not align ourselves with any single social or fashion group.* The magazine wasn't substantial enough to sell, so I left copies in coffeehouses and snuck them onto magazine racks at Cosmic Aeroplane, Jeanie's Smoke Shop, and Raunch Records.

After circulating the first issue of *Flourishing Wasteland*, I felt uneasy. I knew I'd done a half-assed job, writing off the top of my head instead of investigating or researching. Also, who did I think I was? Rereading the issue, I cringed at how opinionated and authoritative I'd tried to sound. In person, I never imposed myself on others like that. That was why I preferred writing—I felt no need to pressure anyone to read my stuff.

I left some copies around our bungalow. Matt didn't seem interested, but Lance read a few pages and gave me a goofily skeptical look. Lisa skimmed the issue with a puzzled expression. "Keep at it, babe," she finally said, stroking my shoulder. "You'll figure it out." When I checked the copies I'd left around town, some were gone but most places still had them all. Where no copies remained, I assumed a shopkeeper or janitor had thrown them away.

I'd hoped *Flourishing Wasteland* would energize my life but, after the first issue, things only seemed to get more boring. Matt was busier, so I saw less of him. He'd started working at an exclusive private club called the New Yorker. The name bothered me—why didn't they call it the Salt Laker? Earning more now, Matt turned yuppier with a brown leather jacket and red Fiat convertible. He started dating a skinny, pretty, Asian new waver and also slept with New Yorker people, including a surprisingly older woman. I wondered how he decided to be homo or hetero or if he just left it to chance.

Meanwhile, my love life continued at zero. I decided to sub-
scribe to *Penthouse,* which was the first porn mag I'd ever seen.
In third grade, my friend from the slow class had claimed his
dad's magazine showed a *Star Trek* actor naked. As we'd thumbed
through *Penthouse* issues, a tingly, swelling sensation had arisen
in me, like I needed to use the toilet in some amazing new way.
When I glanced at my friend, his nostrils were moving like gills.
Later I realized we'd forgotten all about the *Star Trek* actor.

A decade later, however, *Penthouse* didn't thrill me for long.
I wondered if video would be better, but when one of Lance's
friends brought over a porn movie about ancient Rome called
Caligula, I was surprised how unappealing I found it. Porn provided an initial rush, but soon it felt sleazy and depressing, like
watching animals at the zoo.

Lance started bringing home an older friend who waited tables at
Nino's. Barbara had dirty-blond hair, stained teeth, crow-footed
eyes, and a smoker's cough. She could be a hoot, but something
bugged me about her. She was probably in her mid-thirties, and
her life had already peaked. She smoked pot but declined acid,
saying she'd already done her share. She didn't have any sex life.
What if I turned out like her?

I was getting tired of smoking tobacco and pot every day.
Sometimes smoking cigarettes felt almost productive, as if each
puff moved me closer to some cool new state of being, but mostly
it seemed pointless. One evening as I smoked in the lounge at
Nino's, the middle-aged Italian owner approached me. "Why
you Mormon smoke so much?" he asked. Was it just my blondness, or had something else given me away? I decided it was
discriminatory, the same as if I'd assumed he was Mafia—which
I did.

Down in the valet both, I was nearly always high. Even while stoned, the other valet used his downtime productively, studying his meteorology textbooks or cleaning his crusty rock-climbing gear. I tried reading Stephen King while high, but I kept getting confused. At home most evenings, we'd turn on the TV, smoke more weed, drink Barbara's cheap beer, and let David Letterman reprogram our brains to never take anything seriously again. Getting high didn't make me giggle or marvel anymore—after satisfying my late-night munchies, I usually just zonked. I'd thought pot were somehow making my fingernails grow faster, but I realized time was simply passing faster.

While I was getting bored with pot, Lisa was getting weird about it. She always urged us to get high, but I kept seeing her fake it, toking and then letting the smoke dribble away. She acted high, but I could see something wary in her eyes. More than once, I got the feeling Lisa wanted us stoned so we could join her on some strange wavelength she was permanently stuck in.

After several weeks, *Flourishing Wasteland* had received only one letter, a long metaphysical ramble about how Salt Lake City was the "spiritual donut hole of the West." I felt like my life was becoming an empty donut hole too. Did I need to try heroin or visit Rocker Don's witchy mom or rob a convenience store or what?

Chapter 21

L UCY AND TINA HAD BECOME CLOSE FRIENDS, SO TINA visited the bungalow more often. The two sometimes spoke their own Slavic-sounding language, full of phrases like *boosh-kah-lah-dah*. I never had a clue what they were talking about—I almost wondered if it were something lesbian. And then Lucy took Tina skinny-dipping with another young nymph. The two girls seemed to develop instant crushes on each other. I crushed on the new girl too, wishing she'd come after me and make Tina jealous.

The next time Tina came to the bungalow, I put aside my aloofness and sat with her on Matt's green sofa. Not only was I lonely for her, but I wanted to find out if she'd turned bisexual. If she liked girls now, maybe I could be her only male partner. I couldn't imagine taking other women seriously as romantic competition, and maybe it would even lead to a chaotic-neutral threesome—but as I thought about it, a threesome didn't appeal to me, physically or otherwise. When it came to sex, I couldn't deny my chaotic goodness. I didn't care about society's marriage laws or ceremonies, but I wanted one female partner with exclusive, permanent commitment.

As we chatted, Tina was coy about sex, but she told me she was moving into her own studio apartment on State Street, right around the corner from us. We occasionally hung out with the current occupant, James, but we hadn't heard he was moving, and I wondered how Tina had found out. I felt envious—James's studio would've been perfect for me, near the bungalow but a step removed from its gayness and yuppiness.

On the day Tina moved in, I met her mom. Overweight and ruddy cheeked, she didn't look at all like Tina. The two rubber-gloved women scrubbed the apartment as if James had been an AIDS patient. The high-ceilinged studio was gorgeous, with a shiny hardwood floor, rich wood paneling like a lawyer's office, and a cool antique mirror above the tiled fireplace. Tina's mom gave me a few curious, standoffish glances. When she stretched to wipe a high shelf, I saw her silky white temple garments. Watching Tina in housewife mode, I wondered if she had any cooking skills she hadn't yet shared.

At one point, Tina's mom scowled out the front window. Just a few feet away, cars whizzed up and down State Street at a steep angle.

"How can you stand the traffic noise?" the mom asked.

"I like it," Tina said. "It helps me sleep."

I felt suddenly sick. Had Tina already slept here? If so, that would mean she'd slept with James. As I watched the two females clean, I told myself it didn't matter. If she'd boffed James, it must've happened while we were apart. We'd likely never see James again, and I didn't want to miss hanging out with Tina in this cool studio. In later years, the LDS church would transform the house into a convent for the virginal sister missionaries who led tours at Temple Square.

When the Maxim closed, I took it as a sign. Our Capitol Hill bungalow had lasted an impressive six months, and now it was time for a change. I'd been staying some nights at Tina's studio, but we weren't stable enough for me to move in, so I told Matt

I wanted to get my own studio. I said it was mainly because of Lance, which was true, but I also felt Matt and others were holding me back. We'd mastered new wave together, but we'd never gone far enough with punk. I wanted to use *Flourishing Wasteland* to combine punk with psychedelia, the occult, and other underground things. I wanted to blast something cool and original out of Salt Lake City, but none of my friends shared that ambition.

I found a studio on First Avenue in a rundown yellow-brick apartment building. I liked the high ceiling and the large, front-facing windows, but the carpet was filthy beige and the bathroom had no shower, only an ancient claw-footed tub. Now I was even closer to Mormon world headquarters than I'd been at the bungalow. In a small fenced garden a few yards away, Brigham Young lay buried with his second, fourth, tenth, and fifty-first wives. Whenever I walked down First Avenue, the Salt Lake Temple's gothic granite towers rose before me like the figurative smokestacks of a spiritual factory.

On my nineteenth birthday in October 1985, I realized I was now old enough to go on a mission. The idea still sounded awful, but I couldn't help wondering where in the world the church might've sent me. That same day, something insane happened in Salt Lake. Downtown and out in a suburb, shrapnel bombs disguised as packages killed two people. The downtown bomb went off in the Judge Building, where we sometimes ate at the Judge Café.

The next evening, while I was hanging out at the bungalow, Barbara arrived home upset. "You won't believe where I've been," she rasped, her smoker lungs still recovering from climbing Capitol Hill.

"Where?" Lance's face went goofy with concern.

"With the police. I witnessed the third bombing. Turn on the TV."

The third bombing had happened at about 2:40 that afternoon in a parked car less than a block from the bungalow, but we hadn't heard it. Walking down Main Street, Barbara had been looking right at the blue Toyota when the bomb went off, ejecting a man kneeling on the driver's seat so he could reach into the backseat. He turned out to be Mark Hofmann, not another victim but the bomber himself.

The more I learned about the case, the more justified I felt abandoning Mormonism. Hofmann had forged bizarre, compromising early-Mormon writings and tricked church authorities into buying them to hide in the church's securest vaults. Then he'd gotten greedy and presold documents to several buyers, but he couldn't produce the forgeries on time, so he created a diversion by murdering some key players. Finally he triggered one of his own bombs and claimed the fire destroyed the documents.

I especially enjoyed news coverage about the so-called "Salamander Letter." The forger had sold it for $45,000 to one of his future bombing victims, who bought it on the church's behalf. Dated in 1830, the letter described when Joseph Smith had first tried to dig up the golden plates. Instead of meeting God's angel, as the church now taught, Joseph saw a white salamander down in the hole, which changed itself into an "old spirit" and struck Joseph three times. Apparently, Joseph was into folk magic and the gold plates were enchanted treasure.

The Salt Lake alternative scene loved the fiasco. The new Palladium dance club advertised a special "White Salamander Party." On the poster, a Godzilla-sized white salamander invaded the Salt Lake City skyline, its fists smashing the Mormon temple spires. I thought the club should rename itself White Salamander, rather than copying a New York club name. I would've liked *White Salamander* for a magazine name, but I already felt committed to *Flourishing Wasteland*.

Tina told us her parents' next-door neighbors left the church because the leaders had tried to hide the truth and obviously weren't inspired. The current prophet-president, Spencer W. Kimball, wasn't even leading the church anymore. He'd recently had brain surgery, and now he lay sedated in a Hotel Utah penthouse suite. As if to escape the Mark Hofmann mess, he died about two weeks after the bombings. Spencer was my distant cousin, the grandson of Heber C. Kimball with a lesser wife. One of Salt Lake's earliest punk bands had been called Spencer Kimball and the Brainwashed.

"You know Joseph Smith ate magic mushrooms, right?" The new waver sipped his screwdriver cocktail. "He found 'em growing in that grove. How else could he see those visions?"

I laughed. "Makes sense to me."

"He was a necromancer too," the new waver said. "To get the gold plates, he had to bring a piece of his dead brother. They don't teach *that* in Sunday school."

Joseph Smith seemed like a mix of Tom Sawyer and Huckleberry Finn. I wondered what he would've been like as a teen today. I could imagine him playing Dungeons & Dragons. He'd bragged of not committing any "malignant sin" during his youth, but what if he'd lived in this time of rampant sex and drugs? Joseph and his family believed in magical scrolls, amulets, and stones, and he gave my great-great-great-grandfather a divining rod. Heber would don his priesthood robes, kneel with the rod in hand, call upon the Lord, and ask a question. If the answer was no, the rod did nothing; if yes, the rod moved.

After Joseph Smith was martyred in 1844, his body arrived home in an oak box, from which canes were made for his closest friends, symbolizing an oath of revenge against Joseph's killers. The hollow knob of Heber's cane held a clipping of Joseph's hair. The cane could repel demons and heal people, and Heber prophesied it would heal thousands more in the future. I wondered where the cane was now and why my grandpa Kimball didn't use it instead of becoming a worldly doctor.

While I liked seeing the church flounder, deep down I felt disappointed Mormonism had lost any magic it may once have held. Now the religion was all just corporate warm fuzzies and wishful thinking. Modern priesthood holders still gave healing blessings, but doctors and drugs did the real healing, not some supernatural force. Members claimed they could feel answers to prayer, but the days of visions and angelic visitations were long gone.

When I was younger, I'd wondered if perhaps today's church hid all its magic inside the temple, where only worthy adults could go. Why else keep the temple so secret? My parents each kept a small temple suitcase in their closet. I'd wanted to look inside, but I remembered what had happened in *Raiders of the Lost Ark* when the Nazis opened the Ark of the Covenant.

In some ways, the Palladium was cooler than the Maxim had been. The new club featured a larger stage, a better lounge, and lights built into the dance floor. One night, we watched an obscure British band play and then attended a party thrown for them. Hundreds of kids crammed into the house like Tokyo train commuters. Pressed from all sides, the band members looked scared. They soon escaped, and I felt embarrassed for Salt Lake. For me, new wave had become like a spent booster rocket. Lance was right—new wave was just whiter, snootier, more cynical, more British form of disco.

While I was mostly done with new wave, I still wanted to dive deeper into punk. Alone late at night in my grungy studio, I paid closer attention to KRCL's "Behind the Zion Curtain" radio show. I liked heavy, aggressive bands like Discharge and

Celtic Frost that combined dark, mystical metal with hardcore punk's jackhammer rhythms. The show's host, Brad Collins, was the spider at the center of Salt Lake's punk web. As a hippie, he'd worked in Cosmic Aeroplane's head shop. After punk's arrival, he started Raunch Records, booked gigs, and put out records and a fanzine. One night, Collins asked for donations, and I called in a small pledge. Reading my name on the air, he said, "I don't know if Chris is a girl or a boy," which I took as a personal slight.

I wondered how I could get brave enough to shave and dye my hair and pierce something beyond my left ear. I loved punk when it stayed chaotic neutral, but not when it crossed into chaotic evil. Too many punks were thugs and bigots, but I loved the rebellion, the extreme creativity, the irreverence, and the do-it-yourself attitude. I loved how punk could blast away all the mainstream corporate crap, including politics and religion. But I didn't want to get addicted, arrested, or killed.

As I thought about going deeper into punk, I remembered the time I'd peed my bed on purpose as a kid. Whenever my younger siblings woke up dry, they got a little toy, so I'd decided to become a bedwetter too. One night in bed, I let my bladder go. It gave me a hot thrill, but before long I felt cold and clammy. How could I keep punk from turning out like that?

Chapter 22

AFTER RENT, MY MONEY WENT TO RESTAURANTS, clubs, concerts, movies, books, beer, and cigarettes. I rarely bought clothes and, since quitting the corporate record club, I never bought albums anymore. But now I wanted to start building my own alternative-music collection.

Browsing through albums in Cosmic Aeroplane, I considered buying Black Flag's *Slip It In*. But the title song was too sleazy for me, more porn than music. I just didn't like Black Flag—their music sucked, and they were always whining about getting hassled by the police and their own fans. They made sure everyone knew how they worked their butts off but still lived in poverty. And yet if hardcore punk had any stars, it was Black Flag, which seemed unpunk.

I wanted to discover music myself, not follow anyone's recommendation, not even Brad Collins's. I decided to randomly buy an album by an unknown band. As I flipped through records, the firecracker-themed cover of Big Black's *Bulldozer* grabbed me. When I listened to the album at home, it was hard, fast, and angry. The music clanked and clanged, as if played with primitive metal instruments. The lyrics were about things like slaughtering cows and poisoning pigeons. I liked Big Black better than Black Flag, but not by much.

☯

I asked Lisa to start taking me to punk gigs again.

"Hell, yes!" She shook out her wavy hair. "You and me, babe. We're the real punks. Who cares what Matt and Lance say."

In the fall of 1985, Salt Lake's punk scene seemed less strong than it'd been in 1984. The local Native Americans had stopped whoring out their community center for punk shows. Lisa and I attended one gig in the low-ceilinged basement of a frat house by the U. It was crowded, hot, and smelly. From where I stood in back, I couldn't see the band's heads, only their thrashing bodies.

Lisa told me about a gig in a warehouse on the west side. Before she picked me up, I dropped acid. At the last minute, she changed her mind and wanted to try a new coffeehouse called the Painted Word, located in the same building as Raunch Records. But I still wanted to go to the punk gig, so she dropped me off. Instead of lining up with the punks, I leaned against a brick wall and tripped. Streetlight reflected everywhere like silvery, pulsating oobleck. High above in the smeary-starred night, a freeway overpass flowed toward a higher dimension beyond this Prime Material Plane, as Dungeons & Dragons called our physical world.

As I fried on the punk kids, I understood their postapocalyptic leather, spikes, and studs were not costumes but organic outgrowths of their bodies. Bursting out from black, white glowed phosphorescent and red pulsed like blood. Colors and shadows kaleidoscoped across the punks' faces. Their cigarettes made orange neon tracers, not unlike the lines Harold drew with his purple crayon in the children's books.

At one point, I realized the punks had all stopped talking and were looking at me as if they wanted something. I felt uncomfortable, so I turned my head and let my brain fry on something else. When I looked back, the punks were chatting and smoking again like normal. But soon they stopped talking and turned to me again. An impression entered my mind, unlike anything I'd ever felt before, on acid or otherwise. It didn't come as words per se, but the idea was unmistakable: *You can make something of these punks. You have the power.* I felt electricity go up and down my spine, alarmingly pleasurable.

Thinking about it the next day, I wondered if the impression had come from some part of myself I hadn't consciously met yet, the other half that dwelled in my brain's dark side. The impression was not unlike the Holy Ghost's "still, small voice" Mormonism had told me to expect but never came. It also reminded me of the fantasy novel *Lord Valentine's Castle.* People on the planet Majipoor mostly dreamt their own dreams, but some dreams were sendings with insights and instructions. Comforting sendings came from the Lady of the Isle, and disturbing sendings came from the King of Dreams.

An acid trip was like a waking dream. My impression had felt like a sending from somewhere outside my own head. Had the sending somehow arrived from the generalized cosmos or from the collective human consciousness? Or was there a more specific source, as on the planet Majipoor? Either way, I found it cool acid had finally spoken to me, like a reward for recommitting myself to punk. Or was I just being gullible and taking things too literally, like M&M down inside his own stomach with the spiders?

The sending had said I had power, and I couldn't help feeling a little flattered. If I possessed any power, it was in writing and publishing. But the first issue of *Flourishing Wasteland* had sucked, probably because I'd hurriedly typed it in my parents' basement. What I needed was my own computer in my own underground lair, nowhere near the blank white field of Bountiful.

One afternoon, I walked down State Street to Stokes Brothers and found an Atari computer that connected to a regular TV. Even when I added a small color TV and daisywheel printer, the whole package cost only a couple hundred dollars. My dad agreed to give me a loan.

With a computer in my studio, I thought the next issue of *Flourishing Wasteland* would flow out of me. But I couldn't motivate myself to sit down and work. I blamed it on too many people coming around. Even when locked, my door was easy to pop open. Chad brought over girls, and often I arrived home to people getting high in my apartment. I could've written in the mornings, but I always slept late and took long, lonely baths in the old claw-footed tub.

Around this time, Lisa brought me a black-and-white cat, but it soon disappeared. A couple days later, someone brought over beer and, when I opened the fridge, the yowling cat jumped out. Next, Lisa brought me a stray punk. Rob had just returned to Salt Lake after a few months of punking out in Washington, D.C. While Rob was using my bathroom, Lisa said, "He won't ask for food, but make sure you feed him. He's got absolutely nothing."

"I hope he likes cat kibble."

Scowling, Lisa cried out, "We've got to feed the punks!"

Rob looked punk but acted sweet and unassuming, as if forgetting he was in costume. He had a silent, doglike way of letting me know when he wanted something, including cigarettes. However, I liked chatting with him. We were both nineteen. In high school, he'd gotten a girl pregnant and married her, and now she and the kid lived out in Bluffdale while Rob just punked around. He said he was straight, but he'd once let a chicken hawk bugger him. I almost admitted my own buggering, but I couldn't bring myself.

I'd broken off with Tina again, but one evening she followed me down the hill to my studio. Each time she reconnected with me, it felt like the return of the Cat in the Hat, both exciting and dismaying. While Rob played on the computer—he used it more often than I did—Tina and I spooned in my childhood bed. Before long, I'd mounted her under the blanket, trying to move as little as possible. Rob kept his eyes on the screen, but I could see his cheeks turn red. Perhaps that was when he decided to get his own turn with Tina.

Rob and I started fry-walking together. He showed me new things to trip on, like the gothic, gargoyled Cathedral of the Madeline and the aquarium at LDS Hospital, high up in the Avenues. Staring at the psychedelic plants and creatures, I couldn't tell where realness ended and hallucination began.

Sometimes Rob and I sat smoking on Brigham Young's gravesite outside my studio. Fenced in wrought iron, the burial area was littered with dead leaves and overgrown with yellow grass. Brigham and I weren't related by blood, but he and my ancestor Heber had been buddies before the Mormons converted them in upstate New York. The two of them ended up as the only two original apostles never to turn against Joseph Smith.

On the Bigelow side, we were in-laws with Brigham because he'd married two of my great-great-grandaunts. The Bigelows weren't Mormon aristocracy like the Kimballs, but my great-great-great-grandfather Nahum Bigelow had been Mormon almost from the beginning, converting in Illinois in 1839. As polygamy spread in secret, an already-married man pursued Nahum's two eldest daughters, nineteen-year-old Mary and sixteen-year-old Lucy. This upset the girls, so Nahum consulted Brigham Young. "Brother Wicks is a very good man," Brigham told him, "but his wife is a high-strung piece."

A few days later, Brigham dropped by the Bigelows' low-roofed log house and spoke with Mary. "I understand Brother Wicks wishes to have you and your sister Lucy sealed to him. What are your feelings? Do you want him for a husband?"

"No, sir, I don't think I do."

"Well, is there anyone you do want? Ladies ought to have their choice in the matter, for they can choose but one."

"I don't know of anyone, thank you, President Young."

"Well, now then, how would you like me for a husband, Mary?"

"I can't tell, sir."

"Take your own time to think it over. And you may ask your sister Lucy the same question. If you girls would like to be sealed to me, you can tell me whenever you are decided on the matter."

Brigham didn't believe in courting—the Holy Spirit was what brought couples together. Marriage came first, then the romantic sparks. When Mary told Lucy about Brigham's proposal, Lucy hated the idea. But a few days later, Brigham asked Lucy point-blank, and since Mary had already said yes, Lucy couldn't say no.

In the front room of the Bigelow house, Brigham's friend Heber sealed the Bigelow sisters to him. Brigham was forty-five, and the Bigelow sisters were his forty-second and forty-third wives. Lucy had three children by him, and she had lived in Brigham's massive Lion House around the corner from my studio. Mary, however, divorced Brigham and ultimately had four additional husbands, one at a time.

In 1882, Mary and Lucy's younger brother Daniel met Emeline Stevens, a twenty-seven-year-old English divorcée with three daughters. Daniel was already married, but Lucy urged him to accept the law of plural marriage and take Emeline as a second wife. The two wives got along well, and Emeline became my great-great-grandmother, so I was the product of polygamy on both my Kimball and Bigelow sides.

A few years later, Lucy convinced Daniel to take a third wife, a young Norwegian girl. He married her without asking his two wives, which was against the rules. The third wife bore him eight children, but she ruined the family dynamics. When the U.S. government started imprisoning polygamists, Daniel hid in Mexico for more than a year. Back in Utah, he whipped out his own eye while driving cattle and eventually ended up alone on his ranch, his wives all dead or estranged.

It'd been only about sixty-five years since Daniel died in 1921, but I wondered if he'd even recognize today's corporate Mormonism. Heber C. Kimball and Brigham Young certainly wouldn't have, except maybe the clunky old scriptures and nineteenth-century buildings Mormons still used.

When Western Airlines offered an ultra-cheap fare to Boston, I felt driven to visit the city. I was born in New England, and maybe that was where I belonged, not out in the West with the Mormons. Matt agreed to go with me, and my dad let us take his credit card, as long as we both promised to pay him back. A Bountiful travel agent booked us in the Chandler Inn, near downtown Boston. The hotel bar was gay, and each morning the maid arranged our roaches on the rim of a fresh ashtray.

Wandering around Boston, I especially loved the dense, bustling Back Bay with its rows of intricate brownstones. The surname *Bigelow* seemed rare in the West, but in Boston I saw it inlaid in brass. Five generations before my great-great-great-grandfather Nahum, John Bigelow had landed in Boston in 1632. Six generations before my great-great-great-grandfather Heber, Richard Kimball had come in 1634. Both ancestors happened to settle in a small community called Watertown, so they must've known each other. I didn't like being Mormon or American, but I liked having an authentic pedigree. Heber had even taught that Kimballs were related by blood to Jesus Christ's mortal half.

Midweek, Matt and I took the train down to New York. At one funky store, I squeezed bottles of thick, colorful paint to write *Flourishing Wasteland* on a T-shirt. An employee spun the shirt on a device like a pottery wheel, slightly smearing the paint in a cool way, and then she blow-dried it. I pulled on the shirt right away, wanting to advertise my Salt Lake magazine as I walked around Manhattan.

At the Museum of Modern Art, the more Picasso and Van Gogh I saw, the more buzzed I felt. But the real psychedelic experience happened on the top floor. I'd always thought Jackson Pollock was an imposter who just randomly dribbled paint, like a stupid Polack in a 1970s joke. What I hadn't realized was how massive Pollock's paintings could be. Staring into one, I felt an acidy shiver. I looked away before I lost myself in the chaotic-neutral otherworld.

Returning to Boston, I found the city quaint and sleepy compared to New York. In one corner of the Back Bay, we wandered onto the campus of Emerson College, spread among several formerly residential brownstones. In a lobby, I found a brochure for the college's Writing, Literature and Publishing Department. It sounded custom-made for me, but Emerson's tuition was ten times the U's. I assumed Boston's apartment rents were equally as high.

Back in Salt Lake, I got Rob to help me spray-paint *Flourishing Wasteland* in tall, psychedelic letters on my apartment wall. As big as a Pollock canvas, the sign was visible to people walking west down First Avenue. I thought about dubbing my studio the Wasteland, but it felt too forced.

"Another stunt like that, and you're out," the apartment manager said, glaring at me through fake cornflower-blue contact lenses. Lucy and Janet helped me repaint the wall with several coats of beige.

Chapter 23

INSTEAD OF PALLADIUM, LISA STARTED TAKING US TO her beloved Painted Word. Occupying part of a former prosthetic-foot factory, the little coffeehouse served the same wider bohemian scene as Cosmic Aeroplane, not only punks but also hippies, New Agers, gays, artists, and poets. Except for a used-hubcap shop, neighboring buildings looked abandoned, with trash filling their dark, stinky entryways. Under the nearby freeway viaduct, heroin addicts nodded off and transients huddled around barrel fires. Whenever we got out of Lisa's car, bums asked us for cigarettes.

While I loved chatting, sipping, smoking, and eating sandwiches late into the night at Painted Word, I rarely went next door to Raunch Records. Most punks loved Brad Collins, but I felt too much punk pressure in his store. With his pink-dyed halo haircut, Collins was like a punk Roman emperor crowned with a laurel wreath. I'd heard stories of how he and his partner, Daphne, helped runaway punks. But I worried he'd detect I was a poseur, like a dog smelling fear. If I were going to do *Flourishing Wasteland* right, however, I'd eventually have to face him.

When not in her element at Painted Word, Lisa kept getting weirder. Dancing with no music, she'd point upward and squeal, as if something outlandish were passing overhead. Other times, she'd suddenly yell, "I'm wigging out!" and then start sobbing. In

her old Honda, we could play music cassettes, but she wouldn't
let us turn on the radio. "The reception isn't good," she'd cry. "It's
no good!"

Matt was worried too. "She asked if I could read her mind,"
he told me. "And I could tell she was serious."

I didn't bother asking Lisa to take me to the Dead Kennedys show
at the Fairgrounds Horticulture Building. Instead, I dropped
acid, pulled on Scott's combat boots, and jumped into a cab. Two
local bands opened, Maimed for Life and the Kind. I stood at the
edge of the mosh pit, letting the music jackhammer through me.
As the acid came on, I realized Jackson Pollock had captured the
chaotic-neutral essence of a mosh pit.

The more turned on I got, the closer I came to jumping into
the pit. And then suddenly I was in the pit—no one had pushed
me, but I hadn't consciously decided to go in. As if by instinct,
my body started to skank and shove. I expected to feel pain,
but each contact gave me pleasure. I surrendered to the current,
letting it consume me like when I'd bodysurfed as a kid at Aba-
lone Cove.

At some point, I realized I was lying on my back. I wanted
to stay down and just disintegrate under all the thrashing boots,
but a sweaty, muscled arm pulled me up. I let the vortex take me
around a few more times, and then I broke loose and staggered
around, bumping into people. Lights, faces, and sounds smeared
as if I were riding a berserk merry-go-round. My left knee felt
wobbly, the same knee I'd once injured skiing.

Eventually I settled into mellower frying. Chatting with
punks between bands, I heard myself speak in a strong Eastern
European accent. At first, the accent felt good on my lips, tongue,
and throat. When I tried to speak normally, however, I couldn't.

I tried to shut up, but my mouth kept babbling. When people asked where I was from, I couldn't say.

Feeling weirded out, I called a cab. Even on the payphone, I couldn't overcome the accent. I would miss the Dead Kennedys, but I needed to get out of there. When I got home, Rob was gone. I crawled into bed to fry alone through the night, relieved I didn't have to talk to anyone.

By morning, my knee was swollen as big as a cantaloupe. I knew the accent weirdness had been caused by LSD, but I wondered if insanity felt something like that. I didn't like losing control of myself, and I hoped it wouldn't happen again. Was our friend Lisa going crazy in some similar way?

I later heard cartoony-voiced Jello Biafra had taken the Salt Lake stage wearing a Donny and Marie Osmond T-shirt. Then he stripped it off, revealing an upside-down cross shaved into his chest and belly hair. Mormons didn't use crosses, but it still sounded hilarious. I wished I'd just clamped my jaw shut and stayed for the whole show.

Half a block down First Avenue from my studio, the LDS church was wrapping up construction of an eight-story condo, right across State Street from church headquarters. To my surprise, I learned my grandpa Kimball and his new wife were moving into one of the penthouse suites. He'd remarried at age seventy-seven, only three months after my grandma died.

To me, J. LeRoy Kimball had always seemed more like a Mormon apostle than most apostles did. Nearly always dressed in a suit, tie, white shirt, and 1950s-style hat, he was formal and businesslike. His only unapostolic indulgence was wearing a close-cropped Hitleresque mustache, which quirked whenever he employed his dry humor. Technically I was one-fourth Canadian because Grandpa Kimball was born and raised in a Mormon colony up north in Alberta, where his parents had moved from Utah to find irrigation work.

Sometimes I thought of J. Leroy as my Nauvoo grandpa. In 1954, he'd bought Heber C. Kimball's 1845 redbrick house to restore as a summer home. Before long, he was using LDS church money to restore the entire city, which mobs had forced the Mormons to abandon in 1846. Flying out to Nauvoo, Illinois, in 1973, I felt like our family was famous. My grandpa was the bigwig of a major tourist site, and a movie studio was filming a *Huckleberry Finn* musical with Heber's home as the Widow Douglas's house. As an extra, my mom wore a bonnet in a mule-drawn buggy. The only actor I recognized was Harvey Korman from *The Carol Burnett Show,* who played the bogus King of France.

We visited Nauvoo again when I was sixteen. Our family had more than doubled by then, and the motorhome couldn't sleep us all, so the older kids had to stay in a tent. Since that tedious trip, I'd never wanted to return to muggy, remote, churchy Nauvoo, but now I felt like my Nauvoo grandpa was coming after me. From his new penthouse, he could look down upon my hovel below. Would I be expected to visit him? Even if I managed not to stink of smoke, I knew he'd discern my worldly countenance. What arcane patriarchal power might he exercise to reclaim me?

One sunny mid-November Sunday, Matt and I hung out at Travis's new apartment over in the Marmalade District, Capitol Hill's western flank where streets were named for fruit trees. Bountiful punk pioneer Holly had moved in with him, which said a lot for Travis's authenticity. He was gay, but he and Holly seemed like a couple, and not just because of their matching chin clefts. I'd never heard of Travis having a boyfriend, only brief hookups, so maybe he was sexually homo but romantically hetero.

When we arrived, Holly was just leaving. Nodding at me, she said, "You're finally getting your own look."

I glanced down at myself, surprised. I'd dressed carelessly in faded, holey black jeans, a striped beige T-shirt I'd worn in junior high, and beat-up tennis shoes. After running wet fingers through my hair, I'd grabbed Matt's old black Maxim jacket, now shapeless and tattered.

Watching Holly walk away, I felt some tingly attraction. If Maeve were the princess of Salt Lake punk, then Holly was the queen. Maeve hadn't known what to do with me, but maybe Holly could make something of me. Like John Lennon, I needed a Yoko.

Travis and Holly's one-bedroom apartment was more artsy and hippie than punk, scattered with Asian-looking pillows and rugs. In the front room stood a large brass hookah with several smoking hoses. After we inhaled some bubbly ganja smoke, I flipped through Travis's canvases stacked against a wall, stopping at a portrait of the Sub's basement punk. I hadn't realized Travis knew Eric. Done in red and black, the portrait somehow captured our disappointment and hopelessness. I felt a tear slide down.

"Thank you." Travis patted my shoulder. "Thank you."

Out on the patio, we shared a jug of white wine, hefting it on our elbows like hillbillies. While I loved beer, I didn't like wine, at least not chugged from a bottle. Maybe I would've liked the right wine with the right meal, but I hadn't yet experienced that.

"Some of the coolest people are from Bountiful," Travis observed at one point. "You two, Lisa, Holly. There's something real about you guys. You're not just a bunch of poseurs." I felt half-flattered and half-skeptical. "On the other hand," Travis continued, "how worried about Lisa should we be?"

"Fairly worried," I said.

"I'll say," Matt said.

"Oh, hey," Travis said. "That reminds me. I have acid."

Matt rubbed his hands together. "Let's make like the Beatles and day trip."

I wasn't sure I was in the mood for LSD. It was midafternoon, and I hadn't eaten anything yet. My mouth and stomach felt sour from the wine. I was feeling strangely uneasy and dissatisfied. But I went ahead and partook.

An hour later, Matt said, "This acid's no good. I'm barely frying."

"Same," I said. I'd been wondering if I'd developed an LSD tolerance.

"We need more hookah," Travis said.

He led us back inside. It felt good to escape the sunlight, get high again, and relax on a futon. Squatting nearby on a floor cushion, Travis babbled to me. Across the room, Matt sat on a milk crate and browsed through an art book, looking for something to trigger his fry. As I half-listened to Travis, I finally started tripping. At first, Travis's face crawled with the usual war paint. Then I realized he was devolving right before my eyes. Soon he looked like a hunkering caveman from the movie *Quest for Fire*. Then he looked more animal than human. Then he was completely animal.

Freaking out, I got up and hurried outside. I knew I'd just received a major sending. I now knew the truth of what humans really were and how we'd come to be. I'd seen the reality of our place in the universe. We were a randomly evolved life form. We were more advanced in many ways than other Earth animals, but no higher cosmic power existed that considered us any better or more meaningful than any other animal.

For the rest of the trip, I avoided looking at Travis for too long—I'd already seen enough. Part of me felt thrilled about the radical reversal of my Mormon brainwashing, but I also felt jittery.

A few mornings later, someone knocked on my studio door. I expected Rob, who came and went unpredictably and always knocked politely, but it was Travis. Clutching a blanket and pillow, he was dressed in silky pajamas, slippers, and a robe. His hair was messy, his face dark with stubble.

"I walked all the way here." Travis hurried over to the green sofa and sat down. "I've gotta get some sleep! Someone was using a jackhammer right outside my window."

Standing in my underpants, I gave Travis a confused look. To reach my studio, he would've walked past Matt and Lance's bungalow. Why hadn't he just stopped there? After pushing the kitty off the sofa and patting his pillow into place, Travis lay down, pulled the blanket over himself, and closed his eyes. Maybe he really did just need a quiet place to sleep. I felt relieved—if he'd tried anything queer, I probably would've allowed the biological friction, but it would've ruined our friendship.

I got back into bed. A few minutes later, we heard loud clanking.

Travis moaned. "You gotta be kidding."

I remembered the note I'd found taped to my door. "The apartment's doing some plumbing today," I said.

Travis swore, and the clanking continued. "It's worse than the jackhammer," he whined. "You don't know when the next one is coming." He finally sat up and lit a cigarette, and I did the same.

"When we fried the other day," I said, "I saw you turn into a caveman."

This was the first time I'd seen Travis since the acid trip, and I half-expected him to start devolving again. I hoped we could discuss what I'd seen. Did acid reveal similar things to other people?

But Travis gave me a weird look, like I'd made a faux pas. Then he brought up something else.

Lately I'd been thinking that, as with all humans, the truth must've always lain buried inside my head, and acid had simply unloosed it. However, the revelation had felt like another sending from outside myself. Images and ideas had burst into my brain more powerfully than words, but from where? If people were just animals, we were on our own. No supernatural force or intelligence existed beyond the physical sphere.

Sometimes I liked the idea of being an animal. Whenever KCGL played "The Animal Song" by the Europeans, I mentally embraced the lyrics: "We are animals, only animals, still just animals, always animals." Animals were truly chaotic neutral—even evil-seeming snakes, spiders, and sharks killed just to feed or protect themselves. Animalism was the opposite of "Love is all you need," which should've pleased me. But I kept wondering, *Is that it?* I wanted to embrace my psychic breakthrough—animalism would make a cool underlying philosophy for *Flourishing Wasteland*—but I was also considering taking a break from acid. Not only was animalism anticlimactic, but the drug was getting too pushy.

Travis shuffled into the kitchenette. I heard the fridge open and close. Then he called out, "Your water doesn't work!"

"They shut it off for the plumbing."

Travis cursed again. He came over near my bed and put his hands on his hips. "Let's go finagle a bagel. I need coffee."

"You're in your jammies."

"I don't care."

When I returned home from class that afternoon, the apartment manager caught me in the hallway.

"You're out of here." She seemed resigned, not angry.

"What?"

"You flooded the apartment below."

While the water was off, Travis had twisted the spigot all the way open. When the water came back on, a dishrag blocked the drain.

Lisa took the cat. Matt picked up his grandma's sofa, and I also gave him my bong. On Saturday, my dad and brother brought over the family's old blue van. My studio stank of smoke and cat pee, with yeasty undertones of beer and sex. All my furniture was spray-painted in Jackson Pollock style. When my brother opened the fridge and saw only beer, he quickly shut it.

Cheerful as a Boy Scout, Rob helped load the van, then waved goodbye from the front window. I wondered how long he'd get away with squatting there. The empty, dingy studio felt like a skin I'd shed.

Part 3

"Ego is made up of thoughts. It's a big collection of thoughts. *Whose* thoughts? Where'd you get those thoughts?"
—Charles Manson

"The best books, he perceived, are those that tell you what you already know."
—George Orwell, *1984*

"Is God nothing more than a sufficiently advanced extra-terrestrial intelligence?"
—Michael Shermer

Chapter 24

As if hoping I might stay a while, my parents rearranged children to give me back my old basement bedroom. I enjoyed the privacy, but I'd forgotten how noisy the basement could get. Footsteps, creaks, and bumps came from the family room above. Water rushed through pipes, and mechanical sounds hissed and clicked from the furnace, two water heaters, and water softener. Whenever I caught a musty whiff, I wondered how many of my long-ago escaped rodents had died behind walls or in air ducts. I covered my walls with punk flyers and psychedelic posters. To camouflage my smoky funk, I burned incense.

Kids came down only to fetch something from food storage or call my dad and me to dinner. Standing in my bedroom doorway, they seemed shy, impressed, and worried all at once. One evening, I saw my mother crying at her sewing machine. I assumed it was probably related to her tenth pregnancy, but I asked my dad what was wrong. Giving me a neutral look, he said, "She saw a drug magazine in your room." I went straight downstairs and moved all my copies of *High Times* to the bottom of the stack.

Most days, I drove or bussed downtown to valet at Nino's or meet friends. For winter quarter at the U, I registered for only one course, an overview of American literature, so I'd have plenty of time to work on issue two of *Flourishing Wasteland*.

With more time alone, I finally dove into Stephen King's *The Stand,* in which a weaponized virus accidentally kills 99.4 percent of the world's population and supernatural forces gather the survivors for a final standoff between good and evil.

As a kid, I'd loved church lessons about how the latter days would soon morph into the last days. One teacher was a locally famous TV weatherman who made the last days sound like a fast-approaching superstorm. Even as a nonreligious heathen, I still saw the modern world as an infected pimple that needed to pop, and I expected it to happen within my lifetime. Sometimes I even dreamt of dying in a nuclear blast—it felt strangely good, almost orgasmic. *Bring it on,* I thought.

Reading *The Stand,* I wondered how I would've handled being one of the survivors. Would I have gathered with the good to Boulder, Colorado, or with the bad to Las Vegas? Whenever I thought about my caveman sending, it seemed cool at first but then started feeling cold and disappointing. Sometimes I thought I'd accepted animalism, but then it would slip away again. However, *The Stand* gripped my imagination and wouldn't let go. Deep down, did I still believe in supernatural good and evil, with each side striving to lure humans?

On the other hand, I knew *The Stand* was just fantasy. In the real world, Salt Lake's alternative scene was good, and Mormonism was bad. The LDS corporation was run by elderly control freaks who squashed people's individuality with their one-size-fits-all, lowest-common-denominator spiritual product. Alternative movements like punk gave us freedom to reject everything boring and oppressive and become our own authentic, creative selves.

Soon after I moved home, my mother was ready, at age forty-three, to deliver her tenth and final child. She invited the whole family to watch the birth up at LDS Hospital. Sensing I felt weird about it, she reassured me her body was simply a gateway for new human life.

On December 6, 1985, all nine siblings gathered with my dad around my mom's hospital bed. We'd grown up believing our family, as premortal spirits, had chosen each other, and we didn't want to leave anyone behind in the spirit world. As I watched our mother endure cycles of discomfort, it seemed less intense than in movies—after nine births, she must've been used to it. As her first baby back in 1966, I'd overstayed three weeks in her womb, as if reluctant to hurt her and enter the physical world.

Midday, I left the hospital and drove up to the U for an exam, also allowing myself time to smoke. Minutes before I returned, the birth happened. Part of me felt disappointed, but overall I felt relieved not to see my mom go through that. When I arrived back at the hospital, a nurse pulled me into a room to watch the staff finish their procedures and swaddle my new sister. Then I became the first family member to hold her, even before my mom. My new sister felt warm, delicate, and buoyant, like a balloon filled with hot water. I felt guilty for the times I'd scoffed when my parents announced they were having yet another baby.

After the baby came home, I liked standing by the crib while she slept, feeling calm and almost reverent, as if visiting some shrine. I breathed in the odors, not knowing where the store-bought fragrances ended and the real baby smell began. I didn't see how this infant could be a random animal. What if she really were someone I'd known in a pre-Earth spiritual existence, as my family believed?

One day, I tended my three-year-old sister while my mom and the newborn slept. Sitting next to me on a couch, she cocked her head and gave me a thoughtful, concerned look.

"What?" I asked.

"Well . . ." She hesitated. "It's just . . . Mom has a lot of blood in her tummy."

I kept my face neutral. "I think it's for the babies."

"Yes." She touched her own belly.

Later, the three-year-old wandered into the bathroom while I was standing at the toilet. When she saw what I held, a look of horror passed over her face. Despite these early shocks, she would eventually have the most children of my six sisters.

As Christmas neared, someone—probably my dad—left a page torn from the *LDS Church News* on my desk chair. The message was from the current First Presidency, but it sounded like fusty old-time religion: "To those who have ceased activity and to those who have become critical, we say, 'Come back. Come back and feast at the table of the Lord, and taste again the sweet and satisfying fruits of fellowship with the saints.'"

The church was getting desperate. A lot of people must've left after the white salamander scandal. I felt smart for having bailed before the evidence got so blatant.

As if jinxed by me, my closest friends moved home soon after I did. Travis and Lucy lost their jobs. With AIDS starting to weaken him, Lance returned to his parents in Seattle, and Matt couldn't find another roommate. Pregnant with Vince's baby, Janet found someone else to squat with. With no hangout available, we saw less of Chad and Lisa.

By January 1986, we were deep in the winter doldrums, feeling frozen and smogbound like Salt Lake itself. We met downtown whenever we could, but we missed having our own place. Before I could move out again, I needed to catch up financially. The First Avenue apartment had kept my deposit and charged me another two hundred dollars for water damage. I needed to pay several overdue utility bills and traffic tickets. And I owed my dad for many things.

My dad's business was down, so he'd recently laid off his secretary. I asked if I could work for him a few days a week.

"Really?" he asked. "You'd want to do that?"

"Sure," I said. I didn't like working the phones, but I enjoyed processing words and filing papers.

Driving up Capitol Hill one afternoon, I saw a rent sign in a mansion's turret window. It was a studio apartment with new paint and carpet and an amazing downtown view. The place was meant for me, but the rent was $305 a month, double what I'd ever paid. The next time I worked with my dad, an hour passed before I felt nervy enough to mention the studio. Giving me the neutral expression he'd adopted since I'd first left home, he said, "Patience is hard, isn't it."

I tried to forget the studio, but I couldn't stop fantasizing. It wouldn't be a low-class crash pad like First Avenue. Just up the hill from LDS headquarters, it would be my own personal headquarters for influencing Salt Lake's alternative scene. I'd fill it with cool art and furniture. I'd have people over for music, drugs, and sex. I'd pump out issues of *Flourishing Wasteland*.

That night, I called Matt. "Want to share a cool studio?"

"Studio? No way. Too crowded."

"You don't even want to see it?"

"Not a studio."

I brooded in my parents' basement until after midnight. Then I snuck out back and smoked a cigarette in the cold. One benefit of living at home was stronger nicotine buzzes, because I went longer between smokes. I'd started buying imported Dunhill cigarettes at Jeanie's Smoke Shop, hoping the costlier English brand would slow down my smoking, but I still chain-smoked whenever I was downtown.

Salt Lake City still felt fraught with weird, freaky potential for me. I knew what I needed to do—I needed to do *Flourishing Wasteland* right so I could earn some money and move downtown again. Back inside the house, I flushed the butt and locked myself into my bedroom. I felt it was important to use my own computer, even though my dad's much-nicer word processor was just a few rooms away. I turned on the Atari and got to work.

Browsing in the U bookstore one afternoon, I found a journal that made me want to fill its blankness with my handwriting. The green-tinted pages were ruled with faint, narrow lines, just how I liked them. The cardboard-bound journals were cheap, so I bought three.

In addition to vegetable gardens, President Spencer W. Kimball had been big on journals. Each Sabbath, my family used to write in journals together for fifteen minutes. Sometimes I'd enjoyed the outlet, but mostly it was tedious. However, for some reason I now felt eager to try journaling on my own.

I feel like my whole life has led up to Flourishing Wasteland, I wrote. *I wonder if I'd not fallen away from the Mormon church, would I now just be leading a humdrum life, or would something else equally exciting have arisen? Oh well, I've already gone too far to backtrack and start over.*

I got a post-office box at the downtown Salt Lake post office. Bountiful would've been more convenient, but I didn't want a backwoods Bountiful address. In my *Oracle* days, a New York artist had inquired about the odd city name, and I'd felt too embarrassed to explain that, in the Book of Mormon, Bountiful was the ancient city where Jesus Christ visited the Western Hemisphere after his resurrection—or so Joseph Smith had imagined.

The post office assigned me box number 336, and my birthyear was 1966. I wondered if I could have some fun with these Mark of the Beast–ish numbers. Maybe I could pretend my magazine was antichrist or something. Satanic posturing was amusing and intriguing, especially when rock bands did it. Even some punk bands joined in, such as T.S.O.L. with "Dance with Me," a song about the devil using music to control our souls.

During his sermon, the preacher Lynn Bryson had held a cassette player to the microphone and filled the chapel with the tolling bell and slow guitar buildup of AC/DC's "Hells Bells." As the music intensified, Bryson explained how the song worked like a spell. Grinning at each other, my friends and I bounced our heads. I liked the blatantly satanic lyrics, with lines like "If God's on the left, then I'm sticking to the right" and "I'll give you black sensations up and down your spine." According to Bryson, demons helped bands like AC/DC, the Doors, Queen, the Eagles, and Led Zeppelin write and perform their music.

"As far as bringing in converts, rock musicians are to witchcraft as missionaries are to the church," Bryson had said.

In junior high, I'd thought 69 was just a hilariously kinky sex position. But now paisley was popular again with its 6 and 9 shapes, and I saw the 69-shaped yin-yang everywhere. I wondered if *Flourishing Wasteland* could incite some kind of underground movement around 69. If the 1960s had been the white yang, the 1990s could be the black yin. The sixties were revolutionary but too earthy, lovey-dovey, and starry-eyed—we could make the nineties darker and cooler. In the 1980s, crazy things were brewing underground, a freaky mix of punk, psychedelia, and occult sciences. In the 1990s, we could take these things mainstream.

The 1980s are just a warm-up for the 1990s, I wrote in my journal. *I might find myself a major contributor to the movement that is sure to arise in the nineties, comparable to the hippie movement of the sixties.* Thinking about my two acid sendings, I imagined LSD was recruiting me to help launch the world's next alternative movement. Part of me wanted to receive more sendings, but I didn't want acid using me for something I might not end up agreeing with. What if it told me to do something chaotic evil, like the Charles Manson cult?

With *Flourishing Wasteland*, I wanted to bring together all kinds of freaks, not just hippies and punks. Hippiedom was too granola and kumbaya, while punk was too nihilistic, treating disillusionment and rebellion as ends in themselves. But maybe my magazine could combine the best of both, and maybe it could catch on beyond just Salt Lake. On a small scale, I'd spread *The Oracle* throughout the English-speaking world, including Canada, Australia, the United Kingdom, and American military bases. Why not *Flourishing Wasteland* too, maybe even on a larger scale?

Chapter 25

ARRIVING HOME LATE MOST NIGHTS, I WROTE IN MY journal to loosen myself up for *Flourishing Wasteland*. I could never seem to get going on the magazine until after midnight. While I worked, I listened to hard, thrashy punk and metal. Sometimes I'd work till 5:00 or 6:00 a.m. and then sleep till midafternoon.

I'd thought working in my parents' basement had inhibited my creativity on the first issue, but now I realized their basement was the only place I could really work, slipping back into my *Oracle* concentration groove. I typed some drafts on the Atari, but I couldn't resist switching to my dad's CPT 8000 word processor. Purchased used for $15,000, it had a tall black-and-white screen, two floppy disk drives, and over 65,000 bytes of memory.

As I struggled with writing, I felt an urgent need for more sendings. I wondered if I could somehow request them, but that sounded creepily like prayer. I hadn't dropped acid since the caveman sending, and I wondered if I should try writing while tripping. At an Avenues party one night, someone gave Matt a hit of acid, but he'd quit acid because the high was too aggressive, so Travis and I split it. Colors brightened and I felt buzzy, but I didn't fully trip, which came as a relief. I thought about getting another hit to use at home, but I couldn't imagine frying in my parents' basement.

I didn't smoke pot at home either, but Travis and I got high most afternoons, meeting at the top of Victory Road between Bountiful and downtown Salt Lake. Travis's pipe tasted dirty, and we coughed like the beginning of Black Sabbath's "Sweet Leaf." From our west-facing overlook, the view was ultracool industrial, like the Shire after Saruman and his orcs corrupted it. Oil refineries pumped noxious fumes, and flames shot up like a balrog's cigarette lighter. Behind us, a dragonish gravel company was chewing the mountainside raw. Back in my dad's office, I'd work stoned, but the one time he asked if I were on something, I truthfully answered no.

As I worked on my magazine, I knew I needed to get out of my own head and involve other people. But I didn't want anyone to take over the magazine, like I'd let the expensive New Yorkers dominate *The Oracle*. I wanted *Flourishing Wasteland* to be original and exclusive from my own perspective. I wished I could discover a new band and get behind it, using it as a springboard for the magazine and other things.

I fantasized about earning my living from *Flourishing Wasteland*. I wanted the magazine to become famous, but I didn't want to become personally famous, so I decided to use Racer X as my pseudonym. In one of my favorite childhood cartoons, the Japanese-produced *Speed Racer,* Racer X was Speed's mysterious, masked older brother, a role I could relate with. Also, Big Black had put out an album called *Racer-X*.

Whenever I heard my dad creak down the stairs in the middle of the night, I turned off the computer screen and scuttled into my bedroom, like a spider interrupted while spinning its web.

As the writing progressed, I felt psyched enough to make a flyer. Tina and I weren't together, but she let me use a cool photo from her portfolio. Her photographer had snuck her to the top of a downtown skyscraper still under construction. Standing near the edge in a black dress and high heels, Tina stretched back her head and arms against a steel girder, her eyes closed. The Salt Lake Valley fanned out beyond her.

Above and below the photo, I used stick-on letters to write *SALT LAKE CITY: We invite you to explore alternative living on the Front.* I wanted *Flourishing Wasteland* to influence Utah's entire 140-mile Wasatch Front, from Brigham City to Nephi. I included the magazine's name, post office box, and my dad's business phone number, which rang throughout our house. The flyer looked underground but not overtly punk. I hung copies downtown, in the Avenues, around the U, and in Sugar House.

I'd thought hanging flyers would boost my excitement, but instead I started feeling angst. Did I really want to go more public with *Flourishing Wasteland?* Or would it somehow be a mistake? *Last night at the computer was a big failure,* I wrote. *I tried to describe my feelings about punk rock and got discouraged. I've seen it lead to dissatisfaction and unhappiness. Can I pick out the good, constructive things about punk and leave the rest behind?*

Stoned in the valet booth, I read more of *The Stand*'s supernatural good vs. evil and then wrote: *The alternative movement has a mixture of evil and what I really believe is good. Evil because some people use its moral freedom to justify gross behavior. Good because it rejects the oppression of society and makes active leaps for something better. But is this so-called good side really just helping a wasteland flourish?*

I thought about another song the preacher Lynn Bryson had analyzed. I couldn't remember all his charges of paganism and satanism against "Stairway to Heaven"—something about a piper, the May Queen, and bustling in hedgerows. However, one thing had stuck with me. "I agree with Led Zeppelin that there are two pathways in life," Bryson said. "Light and dark, right and wrong, good and evil—call it what you want. Led Zeppelin says it's never too late to change your path. My young friends, that is a lie. If you go too far down the wrong path, there's no turning back."

Bryson used "Stairway to Heaven" to teach us about backmasking, which he'd learned about from Christian preachers. Rock lyrics were the devil's scriptures. If you played certain parts of certain songs backward on your turntable, you could hear secret messages encoded by demons to show off their intelligence and power. "Somebody pushed my pen for me," the songwriter even later admitted.

"This song comes right out and tells us what it's doing," Bryson said. "The lyrics say words can have double meanings. Earlier we were talking about two pathways. Well, here's the pathway Led Zeppelin recommends." He lifted the cassette player to the microphone and hit play. At first, it sounded like gibberish. But with some replays and coaching, we made out the words: "Here's to my sweet Satan. The one little path is there, oh, whose power is Satan. He'll give you 666."

Now that is cool, I'd thought.

As I pondered the song now, I disagreed life offered only two pathways. At a minimum, three paths existed—a light side, a dark side, and atheistic animalism. In reality, billions of pathways must exist, one for each human being. Until now, I'd never felt locked into a certain path. But more and more, doing *Flourishing Wasteland* felt like committing myself. Was it a good path, a bad path, a morally neutral manifestation of my randomly evolved animal intelligence—or somewhere in between all those?

I don't want to blow it in this world, I wrote. *Are my deviant thoughts good to follow? Am I finding my own individuality, or am I being corrupted? Why do I fully expect Salt Lake to become the world's so-called most wicked city, as the Mormons say it will?*

With *Flourishing Wasteland*, I wanted to stay chaotic neutral, not choose a side. But I kept thinking of a line from the Rush song "Freewill"—even if I chose not to decide, I was still making a choice. Maybe neutrality in the Dungeons & Dragons sense was impossible. Neutrality meant using other people only enough to meet one's own reasonable needs, while evil sought excessive power, riches, and pleasure. But who decided what was reasonable or excessive? Maybe humans couldn't be chaotic neutral like animals because our imaginations always made us greedy. Besides, even if practiced correctly, D&D-style neutrality could still get me imprisoned, addicted, or worse.

If only two spiritual opposites existed, my acid sendings had obviously come from the dark side. The thought made me anxious—I needed to stop taking *The Stand*'s struggle between good and evil seriously. As far as I could recall, the novel didn't portray neutral characters. Every survivor gravitated either to Las Vegas or Boulder. I found it telling that my physical location in Salt Lake City lay equidistant between *The Stand*'s two gathering places.

After a hellish week of unease, I decided to push forward with *Flourishing Wasteland*. I wrote: *I'll see if the response to issue #2 leads me to peace and happiness or to further restlessness, depression, and worry. I can see the potential for good and bad. I can see the magazine mired in Salt Lake wickedness, and I can see it as a positive force for creative expression.* I wondered if writing in my journal were backfiring—I liked facing my underlying questions, but was it stirring up too much angst? Sometimes my journal sounded disturbingly religious: *Maybe I should start praying for guidance in the right direction. Would my heart be right, though?*

Wanting to improve on *Flourishing Wasteland*'s weak first issue, I put more effort into layout and graphics. I stole artwork from other alternative zines, especially *Blatch* out of Oklahoma. In one of my old boxes, I found an original comic drawn by a non-Mormon artist at my high school. The piece hadn't fit into *The Oracle*, but now I liked its anti-consumer theme, with a spaceship pilot swerving to miss a giant, floating Coke can but then crashing into an asteroid. This classmate would later illustrate Neil Gaiman's *The Sandman* comic series, basing the character Death on a Palladium club girl.

As my paste-ups came together, I started feeling excited again. On my way to the U in January of 1986, I took the finished layout to Copy Quick. I meant to just drop it off, but as the clerk started handling the originals, I decided to skip class and supervise the copying. Bits of stick-on letters flaked off, so I used a black marker to fill in the gaps. It cost me thirty dollars to make a hundred copies of the twenty-page issue.

With copies in hand, I sped downtown to Café Express. I ordered coffee, but I felt too jittery to eat anything. As punks and new wavers passed through, I sat at our usual table and handed out free copies. Showing the magazine made me nervous. When I got up to refill my coffee, I looked back at the table and saw some punks pointing at pages and laughing. But most people seemed impressed, even a little freaked out.

After rereading the issue, I wrote: *I am pleased. I think the magazine is pretty positive. I even managed to draw good out of punk rock. One article, "Repercussions of the White Salamander Affair," goes against the Mormon church. I should have specified social and political objections, not religious or theological. Elsewhere I make favorable mention of marijuana, although the same article criticizes heavier drugs.*

Some downtown punks invited me to drink beer at the apartment of Chester, a Salt Lake punk veteran. They told me about Alternative 19, a new band they were forming, along with Bountiful punk Holly and her Parisian-looking younger sister. I could tell the punks wanted *Flourishing Wasteland* to back the band. "That sounds cool," I said, wondering if they'd consider a better band name, like White Salamander or Chaotic Neutral. One punk's copy of my magazine looked creased and dog-eared. When he said, "Your voice has so much authority," I could tell he meant it. At an Avenues party, Tina glommed onto me. I wondered if she'd seen the magazine or heard people talking about it. I didn't like her new short-banged haircut, but I wanted her back. Maybe if *Flourishing Wasteland* were successful, she'd want to stay on my good side and not cheat on me. At Crossroads mall, I ran into Maeve and her mom, a short British woman who worked as a janitor. Both women complimented me on *Flourishing Wasteland*. Maeve's eyes still glinted with punkness, and I felt attracted to her. With the magazine, maybe I could draw her attention again.

Just when *Flourishing Wasteland* opened the way before me, like the Red Sea parting at Universal Studios, my recurring childhood dream came back worse than ever. As I approached the throbbing black machine, I thought it was about to explode. Before, I'd always awakened at that point. But this time I kept moving toward the machine, getting close enough to realize the machine was spattering out black oil. When a drop landed on my arm, it felt warm. I touched the sliminess, smeared it between my fingertips, and looked closely.

The fluid wasn't black. It was red.

Chapter 26

BOTH PAINTED WORD AND COSMIC AEROPLANE HUNG my *Flourishing Wasteland* flyer and stocked copies on consignment. Now I needed Raunch Records, but I still felt hesitant about dealing with Salt Lake's punk gatekeeper. What if Brad Collins thought the magazine was lame? I decided to drop off a sample copy with a note inviting him to call me.

After several days, I finally called Collins. "Look, your zine isn't worth two bucks," he said. "Some of the zines in here have triple the pages for only a buck."

"What if we lower the price to a dollar?"

"Too much. The max would be fifty cents."

"I guess it's better than nothing."

I wondered how much money Collins made from punk—apparently, it was enough to work full-time, but he'd only permit me to recoup my photocopy expense. I'd hoped he'd say something encouraging, but now I wondered if he'd even read the copy. Or maybe he viewed my magazine as a competitive threat. Local punk zines just ran music reviews and band interviews, shilling the merchandise Collins sold. My magazine was cooler and more original than *Zionoiz* or *SLAM,* which stood for Salt Lake Area Music. *Flourishing Wasteland* would go wider and deeper than just punk.

I decided to find more stores to carry the magazine. One night after work, I dropped by a magazine shop on State Street,

near an X-rated theater. It was almost midnight, but the por-
nography section was full of browsing men. Feeling grossed out,
I left a sample copy at the front desk and hurried away. At home,
I wrote: *I want to make the underground mystical and intriguing,
not slimy. I'm giving serious thought to cutting off the magazine. I'm
almost embarrassed to promote it. Maybe something is trying to tell
me to back away.*

I cursed *The Stand* again for making me think in terms of
good vs. evil. If *Flourishing Wasteland* wasn't part of the good
side, then what could I do that was? I hoped it didn't have to be
Mormonism. I knew I'd never given the religion a fair chance—
if Mormonism were the good side, then I was screwed. Maybe
Mormonism was the cultural wasteland I should help flourish.
But I couldn't imagine mixing punk's good aspects—its radical
do-it-yourself creativity—with today's corporate Mormonism.

When Matt and Lucy invited me to Las Vegas, I felt relieved. I
didn't like Vegas, but I wanted to get away from Salt Lake City,
Flourishing Wasteland, and my stress about good vs. evil. To
our surprise, Lisa agreed to come. We rarely saw her anymore,
though she kept in touch by phone. She'd lost her job, and it
sounded like she spent most of her time alone in her bedroom
in Bountiful.

My parents knew I was doing another magazine, and they
kept asking to see a copy. Before I left for Vegas, I put one on
my dad's office chair. I liked the idea of giving it to them a few
days before they could talk to me about it. In Vegas, we smoked
pot, ate magic mushrooms, and walked through endless casinos.
The Roman decadence of Caesars Palace blew our minds. We
thought we'd get busted for ordering alcoholic drinks and playing slot machines, but no one noticed we were underage.

Outside on the warm, pulsing Strip, Lisa kept spinning in circles and crying, "Where are all the punks?" After the sun set, she got worse, moaning and sobbing and wandering off. I finally took her back to the motel while Matt and Lucy stayed out. As Lisa slept, I wrote in my journal while shrooming. I claimed I liked mushrooms better than acid, but later I couldn't remember any of my shroom trip except watching colorful, dinnerplate-sized snowflakes float near the ceiling. The next morning, I could still taste bitter fungus stuck in my molars.

On the bus ride home, I felt dull and empty. Vegas reminded me of Pleasure Island in Disney's *Pinocchio* movie. People went there to be naughty, and their behavior turned them into literal jackasses. I wondered if the punk scene were just another version of Pleasure Island.

Back in Salt Lake, I realized the magazine no longer interested me. The change felt so strong that I wondered if the shrooms had somehow mellowed me out or altered my perspective. In my journal, I wrote: *I now see Flourishing Wasteland as a minor, mislead effort. It's not even that good, though I think it shows talent. My grandiose illusions were unrealistic and stupid. I've lost all desire to explore the possibilities of Salt Lake wickedness. In fact, I dislike the city in most ways! If I'm not going to help corrupt Salt Lake, I don't even want to stay here.*

I wondered what I should do next. I wanted to start moving more toward the good side, whatever that meant. I wanted to cut back on tobacco and marijuana. I wanted to eat less fast food. Would I need to make different friends? Could I find something besides the Salt Lake underground to write and publish about? Maybe I could get back into Dungeons & Dragons, or maybe my dad would help me attend Emerson College in Boston.

I like the way I feel now, I wrote in my journal, *as opposed to my worried feelings while doing the magazine.* To my surprise, however, my parents complimented me on the magazine. My mom said she liked the writing. My dad found it impressive enough to mail a copy to Aunt Sue in Federal Heights.

"When's the next issue coming out?" my mom asked.

I shrugged. I'd had some bizarre ideas for issue #3. I wanted to make a stencil and individually spray-paint each cover. I wanted to run detailed accounts of drug trips. I wanted people to send in anonymous genital close-ups, and I'd publish the weirdest ones, like flesh versions of the gnarly, sappy buds in *High Times*. I wanted to dab a trace of my own bodily fluid on each copy. But now the ideas just seemed gross.

Soon after Vegas, I went to a hardcore show at the frat house. Afterward I wrote: *I don't want to waste my effort on something so ridiculous as punk! The people are crude, undisciplined, rude, mean, and corrupt. The music is warped and ugly. The local bands are evil and distorted—L.D.S. sings about death, gore, and devil worship. The people, their attitude, their appearance, their manner—all a farce. I'm more intelligent than that.* I wondered if hippies had been the smart counterculturalists and punks were just degenerate hippies, corrupted by the dark side like elves devolving into violent, evil orcs.

I'd sent out *Flourishing Wasteland* to several LDS missionaries. My cousin in Japan wrote back, *Too many skulls.* My Bigelow grandparents wrote from Australia, *We read every word, but there must be a generation gap.* My friend in New Zealand wrote, *You always did want a Salt Lake underground, didn't you.*

After a few days without the magazine, I didn't know what to do with myself. Even if I'd wanted to keep pushing *Flourishing*

204 ✳ *Christopher Kimball Bigelow*

Wasteland, it wasn't catching on. At Cosmic Aeroplane and Painted Word, only a couple of copies had sold. I'd received only one letter, from some kid who did a lame punk fanzine in my old hometown of Torrance, California.

I wasn't keeping up in my literature class at the U, even though I liked the subject. Instead of going downtown, sometimes I just stayed home all evening in my bathrobe, craving a cigarette until I could smoke outside in the middle of the night. Sometimes I slept for twelve or thirteen hours straight. Tina and Maeve both phoned me, but I didn't return their calls.

When I visited Café Express, people kept asking when the next issue would come out. At first this irritated me, but gradually the attention made me wonder if I wanted to keep trying. I had to do something, if not *Flourishing Wasteland* then some kind of real work or study. *I need the magazine the same way I need a cigarette,* I wrote. *Despite feelings of doubt and trepidation, I still feel interested in the Salt Lake underground, where the banal face of TV and all related American commercialism does not exist.*

I followed up with other stores where I'd left sample copies, except not the sleazy State Street magazine shop. Grunts & Postures, Jeanie's Smoke Shop, and a clothing store called Flashback all agreed to carry the magazine on consignment. After updating my flyer with a list of retail outlets, I hung new copies around town. I made another hundred copies of issue #2 and passed out more freebies and samples.

At a punk gig, someone handed me a copy of *Cry for Action,* a fanzine from Ogden, forty miles north of Salt Lake. It was a weak effort, with a couple of band interviews and some punkish poetry. But I decided to write the editor and see if we could help each other. The fanzine was free but carried advertising, and I wondered if I should switch to that business model.

In the meantime, I photocopied a few hundred small handbills to pass out at Palladium, the Painted Word, and the upcoming INXS concert and Corrosion of Conformity gig. Under an image of a single eyeball surrounded by psychedelic tubes and machinery, I typed: *Flourishing Wasteland has an eye on the Salt Lake scene. Who can guess what it will see?* I listed the retail outlets where people could buy the magazine. I wondered if I could get other people to help pass out handbills.

On January 28, 1986, I came upstairs and saw my mom crying in front of the TV. She'd just watched live coverage of the space shuttle *Challenger* exploding with seven people aboard, including a high-school teacher. As I watched replays of the fireball shooting out smoky tentacles, I felt sick. By doing *Flourishing Wasteland,* was I putting myself at risk for something similar happening to me?

I accompanied my family to help unpack boxes at Grandpa J. LeRoy Kimball's new downtown condo. Watching us from his wheelchair, Roy clapped softly, as if he didn't know what else to do with his hands. When my dad laughed too loud one time, Roy warned him not to wake the church's general authorities, many of whom lived in the new building. I thought he was partially joking, but I couldn't tell how much. My own dryness must've come from Grandpa Kimball, and probably some snobbishness too.

Like a temple's innermost celestial room, Roy's plush penthouse featured gold tones, brightly lit crystal fixtures, ornate furniture, and original paintings, sculptures, and porcelain figures. When Roy's interior decorator showed up during our visit, her brownnosing almost made me gag. Roy's materialism seemed selfish, but I also knew the family had found the uncashed checks of needy patients in Roy's old office files.

Down the hall from Roy's condo, workers were finishing new living quarters for Ezra Taft Benson, the Mormon prophet and president. My grandpa's penthouse took a quarter of the eighth floor, and the prophet's took half. Walking through the prophet's pad, we marveled at the bulletproof windows, security doors, and guard stations, as well as the view of LDS headquarters. I wanted to ride down the prophet's private elevator and explore the church's underground maze of tunnels.

Around the time Grandpa Kimball moved into his condo, my newborn sister received her name and blessing. I hadn't entered a Mormon meetinghouse in nearly two years, but I couldn't disrespect this new person by missing the event. Watching her grow, sometimes I allowed myself some Mormon thoughts about her spirit getting accustomed to her temporary mortal body. On the blessing day, as I sat with my family in the chapel, I worried people would hype me as a returning prodigal, but only a few acknowledged me with brief hellos. I waved to the youth teacher whose advice I remembered best: whenever a boy asked to use the restroom, he'd say, "Just put a rubber band around it." No one seemed to notice when I passed along the sacrament trays without partaking. Watching my siblings take bits of white bread into their mouths, I felt an odd, unexpected pang.

After church, my mom served her customary clam chowder and breadsticks to a mob of Bigelows and Kimballs. I stayed till I couldn't handle any more goodness, then I headed downtown to smoke, drink coffee, and hang out with friends. Church hadn't been as painful as I'd dreaded, but I felt no urge to return.

Late one night, I lay in bed and fantasized about somehow getting downtown commercial space where I could run *Flourishing Wasteland*, host parties and gigs, sell alternative magazines and other stuff, and possibly open a small café. I wanted to call the place Dangerous Planet, the name of a bookstore in a Stephen King novel.

As if in answer to my fantasy, the next evening my freeloader friend Rob showed up at my valet booth. "I have something cool to tell you," he said. "I know a guy who's renting an underground space right on Main Street, a whole basement. It has all these cool nooks for little stores. I'm doing a coffee shop. Other people are doing clothes, records, jewelry, stuff like that. We thought you could do books or something."

It felt weird to hear Rob talk about something productive. The next day, instead of attending class, I grabbed a broom and drove to the underground place. It took me a while to find the right dark, dirty stairwell descending beneath a vacant office building. Slipping through the battered metal door, I felt like a secret-society member. The place was low-ceilinged but bigger than I expected, with a large central area and several side rooms. However, it looked like someone had gone crazy with a sledgehammer. Sheetrock was smashed, floor tiles were broken, and dusty debris lay everywhere. Feeling a creepy vibe, I wondered if the previous tenants had run a drug lab or a child-porn studio or something.

The space made me think of *The Oracle* #2's freaky occult-ish cover, which showed a fanged, double-tailed beast slinking through a mystical chamber lined with alcoves. The New York artist had titled it Animal in the Synagogue, after a Franz Kafka story. I imagined the space as an underground synagogue for shaven-headed punks in bizarre robes and armor. In pillow-strewn alcoves, people would take psychedelic trips and perform bisexual magick rituals.

After work on Friday night, I returned to the underground place. A few people sat in a circle talking, and no one had done any additional cleanup. I'd made good valet tips, so I paid for a case of twenty-four beers. Later, a mousy guy in his thirties asked me for a ride home. When we reached his house, he invited me inside to see his artwork, but soon he was groping me. Later, he

208 ✱ *Christopher Kimball Bigelow*

attempted to mount me, but I recoiled, and the chicken hawk shied away. "Just stop," I finally said.

Arriving home around dawn, I found my dad already working at his desk. As I walked past, he flashed me a stern look but didn't say anything. I went straight to the shower, my chest still feeling ooky where the chicken hawk had spooged, like the time I'd walked under Lagoon's Sky Ride and someone's loogie had hit me.

It was the last queer thing that would ever happen to me. Unable to bring myself to return to the underground place, I wondered what I should do with myself instead.

Chapter 27

MY DAD INVITED ME ON VACATION TO SOUTHERN California with the four oldest kids. We'd leave in a couple weeks, and my mom would stay home with the youngest five.

I didn't want to sneak cigarettes or smell like smoke during the family trip, so I tried cutting back. The first time I let myself run out of cigarettes, I just kept bumming off other people, so I bought myself another pack. After smoking only one, I crumpled the pack and threw it out the car window. To quit tobacco, maybe I also needed to quit pot. One night at Lucy's new apartment, she toked on a doobie and passed it to me, but I said, "No, thanks." She gave me a stunned, hurt look.

After I refused pot, I wondered what step I should take next. *Here go the inner conflicts about good and evil again,* I wrote. *I can't go on with this halfway stuff—either I'm thoroughly good or thoroughly evil. Sometimes I think about religious things, and the conflict brings me to tears. I better not lose myself to corruption and destruction.* I tried to imagine which religion I could explore, but nothing interested me any more than Mormonism did. New Age was hippie pseudoreligion, and not only was I tired of the counterculture, but I didn't trust it anymore.

In my journal, I wrote, *Maybe I should consider going on a mission.* The idea felt at once sickening and radical. Even if I believed in the LDS church, I hated the idea of bothering people about religion. But I liked the idea of completely rebooting myself. A mission would get me far away from Salt Lake City and force me to actually give Mormonism a fair chance. But before I could be called, I'd have to stop all my sins, confess them, and demonstrate repentance for probably at least a year, with lots of praying, fasting, studying scriptures, and serving others.

At Lucy's one evening, I half-jokingly mentioned I was considering a mission. As I expected, my friends freaked out. Lucy shrieked. Travis howled. Tina gave me a pouty look—we weren't back together, but we'd been warming up again. Lisa was not there, and Matt was out of town. That night in my journal, I wrote that I still loved Tina. *We are a match for each other, despite all our mistakes. I worry about her. Hopefully my new direction will influence her as well. We need to erase all the wrongness that's gone on between us.*

On the California trip, I liked returning to my homeland with the family's older half, free from whining, stinky kids. As we drove past our three former homes, I wished we'd stayed in Palos Verdes instead of moving to Utah. If we'd stayed, what would my life be like now?

My dad and I didn't feel like going to Disneyland, so we dropped off the other four and drove to Balboa Beach. In cool, gray weather, we stretched out fully clothed and read our books by the surf, the breeze blowing sand into the pages. I was trying to finish *The Talisman*, but I was tiring of Stephen King. Nothing could top *The Stand.*

After watching the sun set, my dad and I went out for expensive seafood. As we chatted, I heard myself ask, "So, how does someone come back to the church?"

My dad stopped eating and gave me a look, as if assessing whether I were serious. "Well, I think you know," he finally said, his tone practical. "See the bishop. Repent of your sins. Start praying and reading scriptures again."

As if I ever did that before, I thought, *except when you made me.*

The next day, the six of us went on a whale-watching tour. As we drove through Costa Mesa afterward, I saw a punk shop and asked my dad to stop. All day, I'd been fantasizing about *Flourishing Wasteland* and the Salt Lake underground. Wandering the shop's aisles, we looked at the obscene, blasphemous T-shirts and posters. I thought some were cool, but I felt embarrassed having my family in there.

"Come on, kids," my dad said. "We'll wait in the van."

I left the shop with them.

On our way back to Utah, we stopped in Las Vegas. In one casino, my dad let us play slot machines until an employee told him it was illegal. It felt weird to be back in Vegas again so soon. Jonesing for a cigarette, I secretly enjoyed the second-hand smoke. As we walked between casinos, I let loose some *Flourishing Wasteland* handbills on the dry desert breeze. I wasn't sure if I were throwing them away or hoping local punks might find them.

During dinner at Circus Circus's cheap buffet, my dad started talking about the devil and our billions of spiritual siblings who'd followed him.

"Even some Mormons forget how real these spirits are," he said. "Your mom's had experiences with evil spirits. In fact, something happened while we've been on this trip. She heard growling right outside our bedroom window. That's up on the second floor, as you know. It definitely wasn't just an animal."

"What did she do?" The oldest sister's eyes had grown big.

"She said a prayer and went back to sleep. With the Savior on our side, there's no reason to fear."

My dad told us more about our cousin who'd joined the cult. She'd grown up in the same Utah town as the devil-worshiping boy in *Jay's Journal*. At Brigham Young University, she joined a religious study group and met a convert named Bruce Longo. He'd grown up Episcopal in Yonkers, New York, and made some Mormon friends in the Marines. After converting, he served a mission in Uruguay, but he came home early because of voices in his head.

Following his graduation from BYU, Longo received a vision that he would soon become a top LDS church authority. He gained followers, including our cousin, and they started joining hippie communes. Proclaiming himself God, Longo renamed himself Immanuel David. He told his followers they were reincarnated Bible figures, such as Adam, Abraham, Moses, and their wives. They all changed their surnames to David.

Longo claimed he possessed Joseph Smith's golden plates. When his followers asked to see the plates, he clarified *he* was the plates. He warned Mormon authorities about impending calamities and demanded a share of church revenues. He said he was the rightful prophet and Spencer Kimball was an "evil shepherd." After the church excommunicated Longo, he and his group hung out in Temple Square, despite church security often asking them to leave. He preached that God would soon destroy California.

"Here's the thing," my dad said. "These people had real spiritual experiences. But the experiences didn't come from Heavenly Father. Evil spirits can disguise themselves as angels of light. These people exercised their faith on the wrong side."

For over a year, Longo and his family lived downtown on the top floor of an eleven-story hotel. The seven children were polite, smart, and well-dressed, but they didn't attend school. Every day, the family paid their hotel bill in cash, until Longo ran out of money soon after my family moved to Utah in 1978. Knowing the FBI would arrest him for fraudulent fundraising and tax evasion, Longo borrowed a vehicle from a former missionary companion, drove up Emigration Canyon, and committed suicide. When police informed Longo's wife about his death, she stayed calm, knowing he'd been ready to move on to the next world. A few days later, the three oldest children jumped from the hotel balcony of their own volition. One of the younger boys tried to grab the rail, but the mother pushed him off, and then she threw over the three little ones. When only the mother remained, angry onlookers screamed at her to jump, and she did. The children left notes declaring their faith in their father.

Eight years later, the cult was now preparing for Immanuel David's second coming. Our cousin's husband had replaced Longo as the cult's earthly leader. I had only one memory of our cousin. One Christmastime, we delivered my mom's homemade peanut brittle to some Kimball widows and other relatives. Our route included the house where our cousin helped care for Longo's one surviving daughter, now brain damaged in a wheelchair. The cult believed the daughter was Eve reincarnated. From time to time, she tried again to obey her father's suicide command.

My dad tucked a $100 bill into a plate of peanut brittle. As he left the car, our cousin came out into the carport. Her long, dark hair was parted down the middle. The two stood chatting, our headlights illuminating them like a crime scene. My dad had visited the cult before and met the damaged girl, but this time he didn't go inside. Later, another Immanuel David would arise in Salt Lake City and kidnap Elizabeth Smart.

I drove the van all night home from Las Vegas. Whenever I thought about *Flourishing Wasteland,* I felt uneasy. Whenever I imagined a mission, I felt leery but also calmer. While I drove, everyone else slept. It felt good that they trusted me.

The night after we got home, I went to the Berlin and INXS concert at the Salt Palace. I drank alcohol and took speed, but neither affected me much. Late that night, I wrote: *The family trip was important for my spiritual health, just to be immersed in their goodness and strength. Tonight a bunch of wasted people pretended to have fun looking weird and acting obnoxious. I can no longer stomach it. I must jump headfirst into good and quit dragging my feet. It seems strangely simple to switch courses like I'm doing. Perhaps other tribulations lie ahead.*

At that moment, a wave of fear hit me. Lying next to me in bed, the family dog sat up and let out a whine. In the center of my bedroom, I felt some kind of impact, like something trying to smash through an invisible force field. I could feel its extreme anger—whatever it was wanted to rip me to pieces. Cringing, I waited for the next blow, keeping as quiet and motionless as possible.

After a few minutes, I felt brave enough to gently shut my journal, which still lay open in my lap. I sensed my writing had provoked the attack. Part of me wanted to run upstairs and wake my dad, but I didn't dare leave my bed. For the rest of the night, I sat up with the light on, watching the middle of the room for another invisible smack. Wind gusted outside my basement window, every rustle of dry leaves renewing my dread.

"So how was *your* night?" my mom asked the next morning. She gave me a pointed look.

"Not good," I said. "I felt . . . some kind of disturbance in the Force."

"Hmmm," she said. "Your sister woke up terrified in the middle of the night. She slept on our couch clutching *Jesus the Christ*." That night, I made sure to write in my journal while others were still awake. *Last night I stopped writing because a feeling of terror came over me from an unexplainable source. It lasted throughout the night. It made my heart pound and my body shake. I kept an all-night vigil, trying to stay on normal, earthly, neutral territory while sensing greater forces on a deeper level.*

Feeling uneasy as the house above grew silent, I left on my light and lay awake for hours, vulnerable to another invisible strike. I realized the dark side must be real, which meant the light side was real too, otherwise Earth would be a smoldering wasteland. How could I get the light side's protection, the sooner the better?

Chapter 28

LYING IN MY BED EACH NIGHT, I COULDN'T HELP STAR-
ing at the opposite wall, where a panel opened into a narrow crawlspace. Could the dark side somehow enter this world
through the panel? Mirrors felt like another possible entry point,
so I minimized looking into them, including the car's rearview
mirror. Thinking about the attack, I wondered if the dark lord
himself had tried to get me or just one—or more—of his billions
of spirit-minions.

One evening, my mom sat next to me in the living room. She
held a leather-bound biography of Heber C. Kimball, its spine
falling apart. I told her more about what had happened the night
of the spiritual attack.

"I didn't see or hear anything," I said, "but it felt so real."

"Yes," my mom said. "More real than this couch." She patted
the cushion with her left hand. My eye caught her ring with its
ten tiny birthstones set around a large diamond.

"I can't believe how much anger and hate I sensed, in just that
one moment."

"Satan invested a lot in you. He thought he had you. He was
going to use you and then destroy you." At her mention of *Satan*,
my mental corniness alert went off, but I tried to ignore it.

My mom opened the biography to a highlighted page. "I know
you've heard this before, but it might mean more now." She told

me about Heber's experience leading the church's first missionaries to England. As the ship approached its dock in Liverpool, he'd felt so psyched that he leapt the last few feet across the water. Within a week, the missionaries had converted nine people. While they were planning their first baptismal service, the dark side attacked Heber:

> *I was struck with great force by some invisible power. A vision was opened to our minds, and we could distinctly see the evil spirits, who foamed and gnashed their teeth at us. They appeared to be men of full stature who were angry and desperate; and I shall never forget the vindictive malignity depicted on their countenances as they looked me in the eye. We distinctly heard those spirits talk and express their wrath and hellish designs against us. I cannot even look back on the scene without feelings of horror; yet by it I learned the power of the adversary, his enmity against the servants of God, and got some understanding of the invisible world.*

"I'm glad my body didn't get hit like that," I said. Part of me wished I'd seen something, but I probably would've passed out from fear.

"You were protected." My mom gave me a smile. "You know, we prayed you'd have some kind of spiritual experience."

"What do you mean, some kind?"

She fluttered her eyes in her playful way. "Whatever it took to wake you up."

I remembered the time I fell asleep in the mountains above Wallsburg, the town where my great-great-grandpa Daniel Bigelow had lived. I was attending a Mormon youth activity called pioneer trek. On the last afternoon, we'd scattered across the mountainside for individual prayer and reflection, taking along our sleeping bags to sit on. The bugs drove me nuts, so I cocooned myself inside my bag.

Hours later, I woke to a loud boom echoing through the mountains. Sweaty and disoriented, I poked out my head. Daylight was fading, and tall grass surrounded me, blocking my view. For a moment, I had no idea where I was. When I stood up, I saw the pioneer camp just down the slope, with everyone gathered around a bonfire. As I approached, the group applauded. "You were that close this whole time?" an advisor asked, clapping me on the shoulder. To surprise us, our parents had driven up. My mom and dad came forward and hugged me. I'd been missing for over an hour, having slept through several cannon booms.

Though I feared another attack, I felt relieved to finally be facing spiritual reality. My approach seemed bass-ackward, but then again Joseph Smith's first spiritual encounter had been with the dark side. The first time he'd knelt to pray vocally, he felt the evil power of "some actual being from the unseen world" that paralyzed his tongue and tried to destroy him, until a pillar of light rescued him. I also thought of Luke Skywalker, who'd faced the dark side underground during his Jedi training on Yoda's swampy planet.

If the dark side were trying to lure a human, why would it reveal its hate and scare the person away? Maybe it threw tantrums only when it sensed it was losing—if so, the attack on me was a good sign. On the other hand, I should've known all along the dark side was driven by hate, from the *Star Wars* trilogy if nothing else. Either way, I now needed to get as far away from the dark side as possible. Could I keep trying to turn chaotic good on my own? I doubted it—I'd already demonstrated too much spiritual dumbassery. On my own, I'd probably just drift back into selfish neutrality and then into evil, falling under the sway of some Charles Manson or Immanuel David or—worse— becoming one myself.

If I needed organized, lawful-good religion, must it be corporate-processed Mormonism? Mormon culture sucked, but I couldn't see any better options for dealing with the supernatural or the afterlife. The LDS church was probably the furthest away from the dark side a human could get. I knew I'd never choose another Christian religion—if Mormonism were a computer, other Christian churches were typewriters. They were all just "Jesus, Jesus, Jesus" without any cool theology about humanity's pre-Earth life or potential to become godlike. I supposed I could investigate Eastern religions, but they didn't seem very organized or believable, especially not the one with the blue-skinned, elephant-faced god.

If my recurring dream were a sending from the light side— which I felt it must be—that meant the light side acknowledged earthly Mormonism was a cultural wasteland. Could I return to the blank white field, with its few daisies scattered here and there? Could I put on a white shirt and conform to Mormon culture for the rest of my life, with all its earnest, dutiful busywork? Maybe I'd discover more in Mormonism if I gave it a real chance, like I'd given the dark side. Maybe the bland whiteness covered something I couldn't perceive but spiritually smarter people could, something that motivated them to comply with Mormonism's regimented tedium.

What I needed was a supernatural encounter with the light side, something as clear and powerful as my two acid sendings and the attack, something more than just warm fuzzies that might be my own emotions. I supposed the next step would be praying, like Joseph Smith had done, but the thought made me feel weird, especially the thought of praying out loud. I didn't want to trigger another attack—my journaling was like prayer, and the dark side had tried to stop that.

My situation reminded me of a Ramones song: "I just wanna be a good boy. I don't wanna be bad." But sometimes I wished

I could just go back to living my biological life. I didn't want to serve either the light or dark side. Why couldn't invisible spiritual forces just leave humans alone? I wished I could choose my own path based not on good or bad but on what made me personally feel satisfied. However, after what I'd experienced, I knew I needed to choose between light and dark. I knew I needed Mormonism to be true.

"Do you work tonight?" Tina asked on the phone. "I'm looking for a ride downtown."

Tina's house was out of my way, but I heard something different in her voice, so I agreed to pick her up. As we cruised the highway, her playful voice and lemongrass scent made me tingle. When we got downtown, Tina lingered in my valet booth.

"Are you serious about going on a mission?" she asked.

"I think so." I dragged on my cigarette. "I gotta at least try it."

"It might be a good idea." Tina gave me an amazed look. "I can't believe I'm saying that."

"A change of pace, if nothing else."

As we continued talking, Tina admitted she hadn't really needed to come downtown. She'd just wanted to see me. "I even curled my hair and put on makeup."

I could've hugged her and kissed her, but I didn't. When she left, I felt lonely. I wondered if I could get Tina to change spiritually too. If so, I knew it would be a slow, frustrating process. How could we not fall back into our old cycle?

At Lucy's the next night, I felt left out when the others smoked pot, so I smoked some too. It felt good for a while, but later I felt uneasy. If I wanted to leave behind the dark side, I couldn't compromise like that. That night, I left on the light and thrashed in my bed for hours. Having learned the dark side's truth and then still smoked pot, had I opened myself to another, even worse attack? If I let it, the dark side would eventually destroy me both physically and spiritually.

The next time a friend invited me downtown, I said no. Instead, I stayed home and worked late on the computer for my dad. I felt virtuous, but how long could I keep it up? The next morning, I got up before nine and cleaned my room. I thought about attending church that afternoon, but it seemed like too much.

When I saw Tina again, I explained my new views about the reality of the dark and light sides. She nodded along, but I wondered how much she really accepted. We both agreed to stop using marijuana and alcohol. To my surprise, Tina insisted we attend church. I promised we'd go the next Sunday, but on Sunday I slept in and didn't return Tina's calls until after two, when it was too late for church. Instead, we met downtown, got coffee, and saw *Harold and Maude* at the Blue Mouse.

That night, I chatted with my mom by the fire. I told her some of my thoughts and experiences of the last two years, and she pointed out how the dark side had victimized me. *The devil is a chicken hawk*, I thought.

"A few days ago," she told me, "when Chad came to pick up your brother, two of the Davis girls burst into tears and begged him not to go."

"Chad's a real pusher, I gotta admit." I hadn't seen Chad in some time, and I was surprised to hear he was going after my brother. Later in life, he'd become a pusher for strip clubs and liquor companies.

My mom was quiet for a few moments, probably praying for my brother. When she spoke again, she told me that for the past two weeks, she'd noticed something going on with me. I told her two weeks ago was when I'd first started trying to quit tobacco and pot. She told me about an impression she'd received soon after I left home: *Don't worry. He's in my hands. I know him and love him more than you do. Just trust me, and I'll let you know if there's anything you need to do.* Another time, she'd seen a spiritual glimpse of who I really was. "You're a sleeping giant," she said. I wondered what she meant, but I didn't push her for more details. I envied her for all the sendings she received. I hoped I could start receiving some too.

As we stared into the fire, I heard myself say, "The night of the attack, I think Grandma Kimball helped protect me."

My mom looked at me intently.

"It's not like I saw her. But yeah—I think she was standing over by the door. I don't know."

"She's your closest relative in the spirit world. She wouldn't have let you face that alone."

"I wonder if Heber and Nahum were there too," I said, picturing the two stout patriarchs wrestling with demons.

"Absolutely," my mom said. "Without all that protection, the dark side would've destroyed you."

I wondered how much I'd been protected during my wild years. Lots of bad things could've happened, such as disease, injury, or arrest. If I'd stayed wild longer, these things no doubt would've started happening.

When my mother and I chatted again the next evening, I admitted I was thinking about going on a mission.

"I wondered when you'd bring that up," my mom said. "Do you remember your patriarchal blessing?"

"Not really. I don't even know where it is."

"Don't worry, I've kept it safe."

Padding off into the dark, silent house, she returned with a paper covered on both sides with single-spaced typewriting. Even at age sixteen, I'd known the punctuation was bad. The patriarch had tape-recorded the blessing, and his wife had typed it. When he'd laid his hands on my head, I'd felt his elderly tremor. Part of me had thought the idea of a patriarchal blessing was cool, Mormonism's closest thing to getting my fortune told. But I'd also assumed the patriarch said similar things to everybody.

My mom began reading out loud. When she reached the part about developing my musical talent, we exchanged guilty glances. Our pioneer ancestors had carted pianos across the plains, and my mother was a professional piano teacher, but I hadn't stuck with my lessons. Maybe my writing could count as some kind of musical talent.

"Ah, here it is," my mom said. "Your mission. *You will be sent to a foreign country. That is just astounding.*"

Even as a teen, I'd been impressed by that little prophecy. Many missionaries got called stateside, so the patriarch was taking a risk. I'd wondered if he notified church headquarters whenever he prophesied something like that, so the church could make sure it came true. Now, sitting with my mom, I felt an overwhelming desire to find out where I'd be called.

When we got to the part about my future wife, I felt embarrassed. "*At the proper time, you will meet and fall in love with a young handmaiden in Zion. After a proper temple courtship, you will go to the House of the Lord, where you will be sealed for time and all eternity.*"

"Do you think it could be Tina?" my mom asked.

"I hope." I looked away, wondering how Tina and I could ever have a "proper temple courtship." In my mind, we were already technically married, and it was too late.

"Just remember, there's no such thing as one and only," my mom said. "There may be a first choice, but it's not the only choice."

The blessing said I would have children. I couldn't see any way to be good without opening myself to children, but I still hoped maybe somehow I'd be excused. The dark side loved interfering with how and when spirits arrived on Earth, and I felt relieved I hadn't gotten anyone pregnant, as far as I knew.

"*You will be a beacon and a light as you travel through the world,*" my mom read. "This blessing is full of statements like that. *You will touch many people for good. . . . They will want to know more about how you think and act. . . . I bless you that you will always be positive and that you will be a peacemaker.*"

"Can I still be sarcastic sometimes?"

"I hope so." She smiled, her eyes watery behind her bifocals. "Or I'm in trouble too."

Chapter 29

NOW I KNEW THE DARK SIDE WAS REAL, I SENSED ITS efforts everywhere, deceiving humans with counterfeits of good things. Then again, I didn't want to start viewing the world in black and white. Everything earthly must contain some mix of light and dark, even Mormonism. I wished I could learn how to extract the good, discard the bad, and combine things in my own way, but Mormonism insisted on all or nothing.

One afternoon at Lucy's, a member of the horror-punk band L.D.S. dropped by to purchase weed. He wore decadent, postapocalyptic punk regalia. He didn't seem angry or hateful, but I discerned his deep involvement in the dark side. Didn't he know how much the dark side hated him and wanted to destroy him? I felt an almost-panicky desire to warn him, but of course I didn't.

"Man, I feel bad for that guy," I said after he left. "He's so far gone into evil."

"What?" Lucy said.

"How can you say that?" Travis asked.

Even Tina agreed I was being judgmental. I could see I'd have to be more careful sharing my new spiritual perspective.

After Lucy's, Tina and I went to Ben's Café for a cheeseburger. The tiny, ultra-cheap eatery was hidden on the second floor of a slender, gray skyscraper downtown. Whenever punks or new wavers came in, Ben and his wife stared with wary expressions.

Whenever a businessman came in, the Chinese couple's faces broke into relieved smiles.

Some punks arrived at Ben's after Tina and me. One was Eric, the Sub's old basement punk, now wearing long, shaggy hair like Black Flag sometimes did. They said hello but sat as far away as possible, somehow sensing my new vibe. One girl kept glaring at me through greasy black makeup smeared around her eyes, as if she were looking out from inside the dark side. I remembered when she'd first shown up downtown as a smiley new-wave teenybopper. I wished I could explain how much the dark side hated her and wanted to obliterate her.

Tina talked me into seeing *Liquid Sky* at the Blue Mouse. At first, the movie intrigued me—it captured new wave's dark, decadent aura, and the electronic soundtrack reminded me of Laurie Anderson's music. The sci-fi angle was cool, but it soon got too sleazy for me. Whenever a human character experienced a sexual climax, a miniature alien hiding nearby harvested the orgasmic endorphins, killing the human in the process. Realizing this, a non-orgasmic bisexual started luring her enemies into having sex with her.

The more I watched, the more uncomfortable I felt. I could sense the dark side near. "I'm going to the restroom," I whispered to Tina. Instead of returning to the theater, I decided to wait out in my car. After about fifteen minutes, Tina found me. She couldn't believe I'd walked out of a movie, and I almost couldn't believe it either. "I wanted to see how it ended," Tina said. "But I admit, it was kinda yucky." Later, Matt and Lucy told us they'd watched *Liquid Sky* while shrooming, and they'd loved it. I realized that just a few weeks earlier, I would've eaten the foul-tasting mushrooms and dug the movie too.

Tina and I visited Lisa at her mom's house in Bountiful. When she emerged from her bedroom, she seemed dazed and glassy eyed, like she'd taken a pill and then overslept. We tried to get her talking, but she wouldn't say much. She informed us she was leaving soon for Florida, where her dad lived. We couldn't tell if she meant she were visiting him or moving there permanently. I wished we knew what was wrong with Lisa. I wondered if the dark side had anything to do with it.

One unseasonably warm winter afternoon, we met Travis and Lucy for a picnic in Memory Grove. As we ate, I kept glancing up the canyon, as if a black-clad devil worshiper might suddenly emerge from the scrub oak. When Travis and Lucy shared a marijuana pipe, Tina and I declined. But we were still smoking cigarettes.

Travis kept trying to get me talking about *Flourishing Wasteland*.

"Here's the thing," I finally said. "I can't do anything until after my mission. Then it'll probably be totally different."

He let out a sigh. "I still can't believe you're going on a mission." I could tell he wanted to say more, but he held back. Lucy didn't confront me either, but I knew she'd been giving Tina the intellectual runaround against Mormonism.

Matt left a note on my car: *Remember that song from your decadent days, "You're living in your own private Idaho?" Seriously. P.S. Tell Tina we all said hi.* I called him, and we agreed to meet for dinner. "Maybe you can tell me what's really going on," Matt said. I wondered if I could explain how the dark side had tried to get me. My thoughts kept returning to an epic half-hour song by Rush. In the first part, a spaceship pilot approached a black hole, wondering what lay on the other side. As he drew nearer, the hole's suction grew stronger. Unable to turn back, the pilot got atomized—"Sound and fury drown my heart, every nerve is torn apart." Like the pilot, I'd let myself get sucked toward a black hole, but I was escaping before the hole destroyed me.

I decided to type up some black-hole lyrics to help explain things to Matt, without admitting it was a Rush song. As I typed, however, I felt a little guilty. For our high-school literary journal, I'd submitted the lyrics to Rush's song "Losing It" as my own poem. Another guy plagiarized a Rush song too. We caught each other, but no one else caught us.

A few days later, as I waited for Matt at the Market Street Oyster Bar, I felt hopeless about explaining anything spiritual. I wasn't surprised when he showed up tipsy with three coworkers. Instead of explaining my change, I just sat there as they ordered more drinks and gossiped. Beyond a few skeptical, uneasy looks, Matt used his long bangs to avoid eye contact with me. I wished I could've explained that he'd helped save me from the black hole by insisting on safe, remote Dana Point and agreeing with the girls to shut down the Sub.

At home, I threw away the page of Rush lyrics. Another thing I would've liked to explain to Matt—or *somebody*—came in part two. Somehow surviving the black hole's atomization, the space-man found himself among gods warring over logic vs. emotion and order vs. chaos. The spaceman reminded the gods that both were necessary, so the gods made him Cygnus, the God of Balance. As a Libra who could see both sides, I hoped I too could eventually become a god.

Talking later with Lucy and Travis, I realized Matt blamed Tina for my religious one-eighty. Matt thought Tina was hypnotizing me against my friends and using the Mormon church to keep me all to herself. But if anything, the opposite was true. I'd started wondering if religion were the only way to get Tina under control with her nymphomania and bulimia. In my mind, a bargain with God was starting to form: *I'll serve a mission if you'll fix Tina so we can marry when I get back.*

When a store phoned one afternoon to order more copies of *Flourishing Wasteland*, I said publication had ceased and hung up. I didn't want the temptation to revive the magazine. Before the phone left my ear, I heard the caller make a disappointed sound.

As Tina and I pulled away from our downtown friends, we hung out more at each other's houses, talking for hours by our parents' firesides. I loved having her all to myself. Occasionally we took smoke breaks outside—the only reason I still smoked, I felt, was because Tina did. When we invited Matt and Lucy over to watch a video, they declined because they couldn't drink or smoke pot.

One night at my house, Tina showed my mom her modeling portfolio, scooting next to her on the couch and flipping pages for her. Watching my mom's expression, I could tell when they reached the picture of Tina naked except for frosting. When Tina played with my siblings—which she was much better at than I was—the kids reacted with both shyness and curiosity. After she left, one little sister asked me if Tina were a member of the B-52s.

Tina's house was full of Mormon kitsch and garish, mismatched 1970s colors and patterns. Sometimes we chatted with her mom, whose conversation veered all over the place and emphasized weird details. I was enthralled, but Tina often got impatient. One night in Tina's basement, the two of us watched *Sophie's Choice,* which my parents had loved. In the middle of the movie, the lights suddenly flipped on and Tina's mom marched into the room.

"Let me see that movie."

"Mom," Tina groaned. "You're making me crazy."

Her mom picked up the video sleeve. "Your father was right— it's rated R. You can't watch this in our home." She explained that Tina's dad was working late and had felt a prompting that something wasn't right at home. "That's the power of the priesthood," she said. She ejected the video and took it upstairs.

In other words, I thought to myself, *Tina's dad saves her from R-rated movies but not from sexual abuse when she was a girl.* I'd met the man once—he was just another chubby, uptight, white-shirted Mormon, and now he seemed like a prick. No wonder Tina had trouble with her parents. But part of me felt intrigued by patriarchal power. Could a man set standards in his own home and be spiritually warned of violations? Though Tina's dad seemed ultra-devout, he would later divorce her mom and leave the church.

One evening, Tina and I talked about marrying after my mission. I felt so optimistic that I allowed us to cuddle, but I wouldn't kiss her. Not only had we eaten garlic bread at dinner, but I worried we'd get too horny. Almost four months had passed since we'd had sex. I wanted to follow my patriarchal blessing's admonition of a "proper temple courtship," and I didn't know if that included kissing.

I wondered if Tina could ever be faithful to me, let alone to God. I knew it was theoretically possible for her to repent. If I remembered right, the Savior had cast seven devils from a prostitute and then took her as his first of several wives, turning water into wine at their wedding. I couldn't recall if I'd learned this at church, seminary, or home. Maybe Tina was harboring evil spirits too, and casting them out would make her marriageable.

By the end of February 1986, I still hadn't prayed, read scriptures, attended church, or seen the bishop. Of these spiritual hurdles, the bishop interview seemed hardest. I assumed my sins would outrage him. He might disfellowship or excommunicate me, perhaps even announcing my sins from the pulpit.

I knew I needed to go beyond just avoiding the dark side. I needed a relationship with the good side. I wished the Lord would make the first move, but I knew that wasn't how it worked. I needed to grow out of my passiveness—so far, all it had gotten me were tomboys, nymphomaniacs, chicken hawks, and the dark side. One night, I finally knelt by my bed and closed my eyes. At first, praying aloud felt weird, but then it began to flow. I promised to keep trying to change. I asked for help. I said I'd do whatever God wanted. When I paused to listen, my brain felt warmly electric, but I didn't receive any sendings. As I kept praying over the next few evenings, I found I could go for as long as a half-hour. It was even more therapeutic than writing in my journal.

Picking up my mom's heavy, leather-bound scriptures, however, I couldn't bring myself to start studying. I hated reading poetry or anything else that felt like a riddle, and the scriptures seemed so wordy, inconsistent, and outdated. The first time I attended all three hours of church, I found some of it inspiring, but I also felt my old boredom and alienation. Hoping to become more spiritual, I canceled my subscriptions to worldly magazines, ripped the underground propaganda off my bedroom walls, and threw out stacks of periodicals and drawerfuls of punkish pamphlets and flyers. I sold or gave away all my old fantasy novels, rock albums, and D&D manuals. One sister took the Rush albums for her boyfriend, who would eventually die of an overdose.

Even on the radio, I stopped listening to punk, new wave, and mainstream rock. If the preacher Lynn Bryson were even partially right, then most rock was corrupt. According to one rumor, Bryson had been an L.A. music insider until he'd fallen out with the band Three Dog Night. Another rumor said he'd been friends with actress Sharon Tate, and her murder had upset him so much he'd turned to Mormonism. Part of me admired Bryson—he was like a lone prophet from the Bible or Book of Mormon, a warning voice from the wilderness, almost unheard of in today's corporate Mormonism. Sometimes I hoped Bryson's exposure of the satanic conspiracy would goad the good side to counter with something equally cool. However, part of me found Bryson ridiculous and even slanderous. In later years, the LDS church would acquire Rock 103 and keep broadcasting the same satanic music Bryson had warned us against, rebranded as classic rock.

"Why isn't there a Mormon Beatles?" Brother Bryson had asked. "Why do we let the dark side co-opt all the cool stuff?"

He said he was tired of bad people making good music and good people making bad music—he wanted good people to make good music. Rock rhythms and instruments were not inherently evil. In fact, Bryson had recorded some Mormon rock songs of his own, and he sold his cassettes in church foyers after his sermons.

I wished there were a Mormon Beatles too. Jonesing for something to listen to, I borrowed classical albums from my mom. As a child, I'd lain in bed and secretly wept while she'd played piano sonatas, especially the adagio part of Mozart's No. 12 in F major. In my teens, classical music had become background noise, but now I felt ready to dig it again. My favorite was baroque, especially Bach's swirling, harpsichord-infused Brandenburg Concertos, which gave me an almost-psychedelic buzz.

One night, a Kimball uncle came over to help my dad anoint me with consecrated oil for a healing blessing. I thought this uncle resembled Heber C. Kimball, at least in some portraits I'd seen. He was friends with the Mormon bishop who'd baptized Ted Bundy during the serial killer's Utah stint.

As we took our positions for the blessing, the phone rang. It was my boss at Nino's. A customer had filed a claim for car damage, so Nino's was discontinuing valet service and I was fired. "And don't ask me for a reference," the manager said. "You were usually late, surly with customers, and generally unmotivated, almost like you didn't want to make money."

"That timing was not by chance," my dad said after I hung up. "The adversary doesn't want you to receive this blessing."

To refocus us, my mom said a prayer. Then my uncle dabbed a drop of olive oil on the crown of my head and said a brief anointing prayer. Both men laid their hands on my head, and my dad gave the blessing. I liked feeling the warm, heavy hands on my head. I wondered if my dad could hear an inner voice telling him what to say. He blessed me with healing to overcome my addictions and recover from any damage. He blessed me with protection from evil and with courage to go see the bishop. He said I could be a force for bringing many people into the church.

"I remember when you got back from California," my dad said as we chatted after the blessing. "That's when I knew how off track you were. I could see it in your eyes."

I wondered which sin had affected my countenance more, the chicken hawk or LSD.

"It's a miracle you came back so fast," my mom said.

"We thought it might take years, maybe even decades." My dad paused. "In fact, I still wonder if you need rehab or counseling or something."

I realized that, for all my parents knew, I was addicted to heroin or cocaine. Maybe I hadn't been as bad as they thought. If I had any addiction, it was nicotine. I'd mostly stopped smoking, but I'd started dreaming about it—once, a dreamt nicotine buzz even triggered a nocturnal emission.

"Isn't the Lord enough?" I asked.

"Yes, but he expects us to use the resources we've been given," my dad said. "Satan won't let you go without a fight, as you well know. Don't let him intimidate you."

"When you go to the temple," my mom said, "you'll receive extra strength and protection. I hope it's soon. But that's up to the bishop, of course."

After the blessing, I never smoked again. Had the blessing literally healed me, I wondered, or did I just try harder after the blessing, wanting to help it come true? Tina claimed she'd totally quit smoking too, and I hoped it was the truth.

Chapter 30

YOU'RE BEING PARANOID," TINA SAID. "WE'RE JUST going to a party."

"But you dated this guy."

"Well, I'm dating you now. I'm not his date. I just want to meet some modeling people he knows."

"I wasn't going to ask, but did you two ever have sex?"

Tina gave an irritated screech. "Of course not. He asked, and I said no."

Did Tina really not understand why I was upset? She'd already admitted quitting smoking had made her bulimia worse—what if it were also intensifying her nymphomania? What if any partyers offered her cocaine or alcohol? Lately she'd seemed depressed, which made her a prime temptation target. She didn't have spiritual strength yet. She hadn't experienced anything supernatural, so why was she even dabbling in religion, except to please me?

When Tina called the next day, I restrained myself from asking how the party went.

"Guess who I saw on the bus today?" She sounded too bubbly.

"Who?" I kept my voice flat.

"My bishop! And I made an appointment."

I was stunned. As soon as we hung up, I found the ward list and called Bishop Cutler. My parents' bishop wore a toupee, and he cleaned carpets for a living, with my brother as his employee.

I wondered how a carpet cleaner earned enough money to live up on the Bountiful bench, especially with church taking so much of his time.

As a child, I'd often thought of the church as Heavenly Father's bank, especially during the annual tithing settlement. My dad wore the same business suits and ties to church as he did to his bank job. In the priesthood, he held the numerical office of seventy, which made his church job seem analogous to his bank job.

"I've been inactive for two years," I told Bishop Cutler, feeling like we were discussing my default on a loan. "*Very* inactive."

"Your dad told me about your experience. So now you know Satan's real, huh?"

Beginning my confession, I felt calmer than I'd expected, almost as if I were discussing someone else. Wanting to be thorough, I started way back with the prebaptismal strip poker and moved up through Doug, including the couple of times he'd pushed my head down and then refused to reciprocate. Nodding, the bishop seemed to already know about Doug, who was also infamous for vrooming motorcycles around the neighborhood, spray-painting graffiti on curbs, taking little girls into the bushes to pull down their underpants, and burning up a dry field near some homes.

As I divulged more recent sins, occasionally the bishop asked how many times something had happened or how long ago. No matter what I confessed, his expression stayed calm, almost bored. "The last one was just a few weeks ago," I said, and then I told him about the chicken hawk. "It was an ambush—I didn't even climax." I'd looked forward to sharing this evidence of my straightness.

When I was done, the bishop leaned forward and clasped his hands on the desktop. "It sounds like you've mostly given in to

236 * Christopher Kimball Bigelow

pressure from others, as opposed to seeking out sinful things or trying to corrupt other people."

"I guess I was open to anything that came along." Inwardly, I felt a twinge about *Flourishing Wasteland*, knowing I'd intended to draw people deeper into the dark side, including younger kids, perhaps becoming a chicken hawk of their minds.

The bishop started talking about the Savior's atonement and how I should feel godly sorrow for my sins. "When we sin, the devil has claim on us," he said. "He gets to punish us, unless we repent and someone takes the punishment for us, and that's the Savior."

As he continued, I thought about repentance. After my encounter with the devil, I knew the Savior had to be real too. But I wasn't sure about feeling godly sorrow. To me, repentance felt like simply admitting, *OK, I get it now.* I'd performed reasonable—perhaps even courageous—experiments. Sometimes I'd felt anxious and queasy, but I didn't regret the experiments, because how else could I have learned? It wasn't my fault Mormonism failed to engage me with anything cool like the Beatles, *Star Wars,* Dungeons & Dragons, or Stephen King. Maybe I'd needed LSD to prep my imagination for LDS, like Joseph Smith had needed folk magic to prepare him for prophethood. Maybe I'd needed sexual misadventures to understand I was a monogamous heterosexual.

I wished I hadn't made things harder for my parents, my roommate Virgil, or Scott down in Dana Point, but my only real sorrow had come from Tina's cheating, not from my own experiments. I felt grateful for the Savior's sacrifice, but I saw him as a superhuman who'd known what he was getting into and had successfully performed his role, not as someone I needed to feel bad about personally making suffer. Maybe I needed to feel sorry for not feeling as sorry as I should. If I sinned in the future, however, I knew I'd feel more guilt and remorse. I'd be abandoning myself to the dark side even though I knew how much it hated

me. The thought of backsliding into the dark side's control terrified me.

Bishop Cutler outlined my repentance plan. No big surprises
there—I needed to attend church meetings, fast, pray, study, and
serve others.

"Now, what about girls? Do you have a girlfriend now?"

"Yes."

"Is it the same girl we've been discussing?"

"Yes. But she's seeing her bishop too." I wondered exactly what
Tina would confess. Did she even know how many people she'd
fornicated with?

Leaning back in his chair, the bishop looked at me. "I'm glad
you're helping her. But that's going to be your biggest challenge."
He told me about his rule of three. Tina and I could touch
while we were alone, but not for a long time. We could be alone
together for a long time, but not touching. We could touch for a
long time, but not while we were alone.

The bishop opened a drawer, took out a missionary application, and uncapped his pen. "If you stay on track, we can get you
out serving the Lord within a few months."

I felt surprised. He hadn't said anything about disfellowship-
ment or excommunication, just not to partake of the sacrament
until we met again. I'd been thinking a mission would be my
reward for coming back, but what if it were actually a punishment for my sins, like being sent off to spiritual reform school?

As I left, the bishop handed me a book to read, Spencer W.
Kimball's *The Miracle of Forgiveness*. Driving home, I felt warm,
tingly, and relieved. The Lord must've helped the bishop discern
the depth of my conversion. When it came to bishops, I'd been
lucky. I'd heard of strict bishops who grilled boys until they cried.
But my previous bishop had said, "I'm not going to ask if you
masturbate. Just be aware it can become a compulsive habit. If
you need help, come see me." At that bishop's house, I'd seen *The*

Joy of Sex sitting out on a bookshelf. My parents had kept their copy hidden in their closet, under my dad's temple bag. I could still picture the illustrations of hairy seventies sex.

To my amazement, the bishop saw me only once more before signing my missionary papers. My next hurdle was to meet with the stake president, but the bishop said I didn't need to confess my sins again. I'd also have to visit the doctor and dentist and take a language aptitude test.

When Tina told her parents we'd both seen our bishops, her dad accused us of mocking them.

"We really did," I said.

They looked at me in shock. Then the dad fell on his knees. "It's true," he gasped. "I can see it in your eyes."

We talked for a couple of hours. I didn't like how Tina's dad gave me all the credit and attention, almost ignoring Tina. He sent me home with an armful of religious books. The next Sunday, he took me along to visit his assigned families in the ward. At each house, he asked me to retell my conversion story. As we drove home, he said, "Tina has a hard time, but her heart is good."

"Yeah. If anything, she's too generous."

He didn't give any sign of taking my meaning. "To some," he said, "it's given by the Holy Ghost to know. That's you. To others, it's given to believe on the words of those who know. That's Tina, believing in you."

I liked thinking of myself as Tina's spiritual anchor. No mere human could get her under control, but with the Lord's help maybe I could. However, I didn't like the idea of a "Holy Ghost." It was a corny name and a weird, unclear concept. The Holy Ghost was supposedly a separate personage from God with its own humanoid spirit body, and somehow this body could simultaneously enter the hearts of millions of mortals. As far as I knew, I still hadn't felt the Holy Ghost—or if I had, it felt the same as my own emotions. Maybe I'd understand it better once I got my first real sending from the light side.

I wondered how Tina and I would survive my mission. Could my letters sustain her for two whole years? Would I worry and miss her too much? If she couldn't stay churched while I was gone, maybe that would be a sign she wasn't spiritually strong enough to marry me. I wished we could just get married now and serve a mission together—with my understanding and Tina's people skills, we would've made an excellent proselyting team. Young Mormon couples had served together in the past, but the church no longer allowed such free agency.

As we stretched out before her basement fireplace, I explained to Tina how the fight between good and evil would intensify before the Second Coming. Since seeing the bishop, I'd been getting more psyched about Mormon theology. LSD must be a tool of the dark side, but maybe it had opened my mind so I could better imagine the eternal spiritual dimension. I told Tina how she and I would continually progress together in spheres beyond this earthly one. Eventually we'd create planets where our spirit-children could undergo their own mortal tests.

I think Tina and I chose each other as mates in the premortal existence, I wrote in my journal. *I can't imagine further progress without her, not even during mortality.*

When I saw the bishop again, he gave me the go-ahead to start taking the sacrament. As a child, I'd gobbled the bread and slurped the water hundreds of times, but now I tried to partake with prayerful thoughts.

My parents bought me a leather-bound quad containing all four books of Mormon scripture. I asked them for seventy-five dollars so I could buy one for Tina, and they added it to my tab. My quad was dark brown with gilt trim, and Tina's was green with silver trim. Our full names were embossed on the front covers. Even with such a nice volume, however, I still found it tedious to read scriptures. I preferred more contemporary religious books.

On the first Sunday of the month, I fasted. As a kid, I'd never understood why Heavenly Father wanted people to suffer without food and water for twenty-four hours. Now I tried to view it as a way of saying, "Hey, God, I'm serious." After having struggled to quit smoking, I didn't find it too hard to resist my food appetite for just one day. My prayers felt stronger while I was fasting, but I took naps to make the time pass quicker.

As I read Spencer W. Kimball's *The Miracle of Forgiveness*, I found it unexpectedly blunt. Published in 1969, the book was obviously a reaction against hippies and the sexual revolution, and Spencer would later admit to overstating some things. As a kid, I'd always had warm, fuzzy impressions of cousin Spencer. When I was three, he'd stood in line behind my mother at the airport. Wrangling both me and my baby brother, she'd suddenly realized she was at the wrong gate. Spencer grabbed the baby and ran with us to the correct gate. My cardiologist grandfather was upset when he heard about it, because of Spencer's heart condition.

Around the time Spencer became prophet, my grandpa Kimball took me to visit him at home. I was six or seven. Spencer lived in a cramped Salt Lake neighborhood, his brick home much older and smaller than my Palos Verdes house. In the driveway, I saw a bodyguard sitting in a car. Spencer came to the door wearing slippers and a red cardigan over his open-collared white shirt. He took us to his study, which was smaller than my parents' master bathroom. The two cousins talked mainly about my grandfather's restoration of the 1840s Mormon town of Nauvoo, Illinois. I'd later learn the two church presidents before Spencer had almost ruined my grandfather's project, but Spencer gave him back some money and autonomy.

As I glanced around the room, I saw a shelf of what looked like journals, and I wondered if he kept a vegetable garden too, as he often instructed members to do. At one point, Spencer opened a box of fancy chocolates and offered them to us. Biting into mine, I found it squishy pink, so I hid it in my fist, hoping to throw it away later. The next time the box came around, I tried for a simple caramel, but I got beige paste studded with nuts and coconut shreds. By the time the visit ended, my fist oozed brown from every seam. Chuckling, Spencer took me to the bathroom. Part of me felt ashamed, like I'd messed my pants or something, but another part felt it wasn't my fault the candy was so gloopy and gross. He helped me dump the melty mass into the trashcan, and then he washed my young hand between his bloated, splotchy old hands.

After *The Empire Strikes Back* came out in 1980, I'd loved the comparisons of Spencer with Yoda. Both were short, big-eared, wrinkle-faced, and mostly bald, with wisps of white hair. Spencer had lost some vocal chords to throat cancer, so he sounded croaky like Yoda. Spencer told Mormons, "Trying is not sufficient. Do it!" Yoda told Luke, "Do or do not. There is no try."

In *Miracle of Forgiveness,* Spencer wrote that sex outside marriage was the sin next to murder. Murder destroyed someone's physical body too early, while unmarried sex risked creating it too early. I could see rape, incest, and child molesting as next to murder, and even adultery seemed almost that bad. But were Tina and I

242 ＊ *Christopher Kimball Bigelow*

worse than robbers, kidnappers, and torturers? If so, I couldn't see it.

Spencer taught additional things I didn't like. Couples should not kiss until late in courtship, and even then their kisses should be "free from sex and have holy meaning." He warned against the twin evils of necking and petting, which sounded like corny 1950s party games. Losing one's virtue was worse than death—any true Latter-day Saint parent would rather bury a child than have them lose their chastity. I felt glad my parents weren't that hardcore. However, I liked Spencer's teaching that "soul mates are fiction and an illusion." If Tina didn't stick with Mormonism while I was gone, I could find someone else. Spencer said any good man and woman could make a successful marriage, if they put in the effort.

When I read the "Crime Against Nature" chapter, I felt relieved homosexuality wasn't my issue. Spencer put it on the same spectrum as bestiality. He said masturbation could lead to homosexual behavior. Part of me thought that sounded ridiculous, but I could also see how masturbating was like being gay with yourself. All my crushes were female. However, while handling my own male equipment, I'd sometimes imagined partnering with a faceless projection of my older self. But what about people who were naturally gay? If Lisa, Lance, and Travis felt the same about their own sex as I did about my opposite, I didn't see how God could blame them. Or were they just being rebellious and self-indulgent? Were they deceived by the dark side? I decided I didn't need to worry about it. The gay and Mormon worlds would never collide. Why would a homosexual ever want to be Mormon, or vice versa?

Spencer talked about the point of no return, making me wonder how close to it I'd come. Sometimes I wished I'd experienced more while I was still spiritually naïve, such as witchcraft, group sex, and needle drugs. But I'd probably gone as far as I could go and still turn back. I felt glad I hadn't started making money—with enough money, I probably would've stayed on the dark side. I might've ultimately become a son of perdition, rejecting God even after experiencing the full cosmic truth. Once God no longer needed the dark side to provide earthly opposition, perhaps the sons and daughters of perdition would disintegrate as individual beings, their raw intelligence returning to the universe's unorganized gray matter like failed pottery spins folded back into the raw clay heap.

My favorite part came in Spencer's chapter about murder. Riding his mule down a lonely road, an early Mormon apostle met Cain, who still walked the Earth as a cursed immortal. Over the millennia, Earth's first murderer had become extra-tall, dark-skinned, and hairy like a Sasquatch or Wookiee. Cain admitted to the apostle that he was miserable—he kept trying to die, but he could not. He had no choice but to continue his earthly mission to destroy people's souls. When the apostle rebuked him, Cain slunk away.

This made theological sense to me. To provide a fair, balanced test, the earthly sphere required equal measures of light and dark. If Mormonism were correct, four good immortals currently roamed the planet, including John the Beloved and the Three Nephites, so evil immortals must roam the planet too. My grandpa Kimball's patriarchal blessing had said the Three Nephites would minister to him. I wondered when they'd done so and if my grandfather had known when it was happening.

I wished I could meet one of the good immortals.

Chapter 31

O N A SATURDAY, THE WARD'S TEEN BOYS AND THEIR dads met for lunch. When we finished eating, the group prayed to start a fast for guidance about our mission preparations. The next day, we broke our fast with lunch at the bishop's house and bore our testimonies.

When it was my turn, I stood before the group wearing black jeans, a black homemade shirt, and a tie borrowed from my dad. Hanging out with Mormons, sometimes I still felt like I'd just staggered wet and disheveled into their storm shelter. As I talked, I felt almost weepy. "There's a big battle coming up," I quavered. "Salt Lake is headquarters of the true religion, so of course the devil wants to make it his headquarters of evil." Some listeners gave me perplexed, uneasy looks.

Chatting later with white-shirted fathers and sons, I didn't mind their company, but—as with punks—I thought of them as *them*. I wondered if I'd ever find my own people. I hadn't felt as angry and decadent as the coolest punks and new wavers, but I wasn't naturally pure and sheepish like most Mormons. I supposed I didn't have the stomach for either too much good or too much evil. I hoped I wasn't one of those lukewarm people Jesus would spit out.

When my mom took me to buy church clothes, it reminded me of school shopping. The next Sunday, I showed up at Tina's house in khakis, a white shirt, and a tie. She said I looked like a dad.

✿

As I pushed forward, I felt surprised how full of Mormonism I already was. I'd absorbed more than I'd realized, and now it was finally jelling in my mind. Did I acquire the knowledge during premortality or just from growing up in the church? On the other hand, sometimes I felt like I was jumping too fast into Mormonism. After going through a messy breakup with the dark side, was I now in a rebound relationship? Could a person swing from chaotic neutral to lawful good as fast as I was doing?

I kept trying to imagine myself as a lifelong active Mormon. Would I ever feel culturally at home among churchgoers? Sometimes I envied people whose natural personalities dovetailed with the church's conservative, paint-by-numbers mindset, people who loved following traditions and authority. I wanted to develop faith and humility, but I also wanted to keep my individuality. Could I ever fulfill my own creativity within Mormonism, or must I become the human equivalent of an ant or a bee? I felt no desire to progress up the priesthood hierarchy, but maybe I could do something creatively independent within Mormon culture, like the magazines I'd done on Dungeons & Dragons and the Salt Lake underground.

I admired how organized and efficient the church could be. I felt no doubt Mormonism was the Earth's truest organized religion. But I couldn't help thinking the church had failed me more than I'd failed it. For a religion that talked so much about people's free agency, the LDS corporation allowed almost no individual choice or initiative within the church. Everything was dictated by Salt Lake headquarters, down to the scratchy burlap on meetinghouse walls. Members must do everything the corporate way and become identically perfect. Where corporate headquarters didn't spell things out, Mormon culture filled in the blanks.

I couldn't comprehend devout members who loved the church exactly how it was now, as if the Lord had whispered every detail into the minds of church bureaucrats. Did the Lord really want the church to follow so many bland, standardized rules and conventions? Did he want Mormons behaving so much like Oompa-Loompas, filling their time with submissive busywork? Did he want Mormons so fully embracing American suburban and consumer lifestyles? Did he want the church to behave so much like a control-freak corporation, squashing all experimentation, innovation, and dissent? Did he want Mormonism to draw such a firm line between itself and the world, defining itself culturally more by what it wasn't than by what it was?

I wondered if the dark side had helped trap Mormonism inside its vanilla bubble, tempting members and leaders to be too cautious and controlling. Or maybe the 1800s hardships had scared the Mormons into their corporate shell. Maybe the church had overcorrected from weirdness to blandness and would eventually balance out—or maybe Mormonism, by its nature, would always be either too weird or too bland. Maybe true-blue Mormons were so focused on the pre-Earth and post-Earth lives that they didn't mind how insipid Mormonism made their Earth lives. On the other hand, maybe Mormonism must be like plain white rice so people around the world could add their own cultural sauces, meats, and spices, although I questioned how much the corporation actually allowed that. Maybe, like the hobbits of Middle Earth, Mormons needed to be culturally simple and smallminded so they could defeat the dark side instead of getting corrupted by it.

I wished the good side could feel as imaginative and adventurous as the dark side had. I wished Mormonism could be psychedelic and bohemian. Part of me felt embarrassed I'd ever taken punk seriously, but I also wished a punk version of Mormonism could exist, something wild, passionate, and uncompromisingly do-it-yourself. Joseph Smith and Jesus Christ had both been punkish, rebelling against human authority's unrighteous dominion, but now the church corporation had become another bastion of human authority. Was it possible to bring some punk spirit back into Mormonism? I wondered how much rebellion and conformity my Libra personality could balance within Mormonism. I knew I must always qualify to enter the temple, but beyond those basic standards I hoped I could resist white-shirt Mormon culture.

Following sacrament meeting one Sunday, all the teens gathered for a special presentation by some kids from a local drug-rehab center. One of the guys, Todd, had grown up in the old part of our ward, but he was younger than me, so I hadn't hung out much with him.

"All right, let's get real," Todd said to our group. "I want this to be totally open and honest, so I want all the adults to leave the room. That includes you, Mike." He gestured at their rehab counselor.

Blinking at each other, all the adults filed out.

As a tall, thin Hispanic boy told his drug story, I realized it was Miguel, the runaway punk nabbed by the police at the Sub. With his mohawk gone, he looked like a shorn sheep. His Mormon-style white shirt looked dingy, and it was tight across the chest and short in the sleeves. I made eye contact with him, but I must've been too far out of context for him to recognize me.

When it was Todd's turn, he talked about all the things he'd done wrong, followed by a simple "Don't do likewise." He lit up most when he expressed his love of LSD. "You guys gotta do what you gotta do," he told us. "No one else can figure it out for you." I agreed, but I felt an unhumble vibe from him. One of my sisters said she'd heard Todd had been involved in devil worship. I wondered if he were still a double agent for the dark side.

On a Sunday evening, Tina and I went with our parents to hear apostle Neal A. Maxwell speak at a chapel across from the U. Known for his deep, alliterative sermons, Elder Maxwell was my mom's favorite, and I'd sometimes enjoyed his talks too. In general conference, he said things like, "Traversing these truths requires more than a casual stroll up sloping foothills; they take us instead up the breathtaking ridges of reality to an Everest of understanding. On a clear day, we can see forever!"

I expected an overflow congregation, but only about forty people came. We sat right in front of the pulpit, close enough I could see Elder Maxwell's acne scars, which were deeper than mine. At one point as he spoke, Elder Maxwell looked straight down at me, and some kind of energy vibrated between us. The apostle's expression turned weirdly intense, and I felt like I was glowing. The sensation lasted only a few seconds, and I almost let out a gasp. No one else seemed to notice anything—Elder Maxwell hadn't missed a beat. As I sat there feeling warm and amazed, I realized Elder Maxwell had seen my true spiritual nature, and thus I'd glimpsed it too.

Over the next few days, I marveled about my first sending from the light side. It was cooler than I'd hoped—I'd been expecting simply an inner voice or prompting. I wondered if the sending had something to do with my mission call. The twelve apostles decided all the worldwide calls, and maybe they'd call me as the first modern-day missionary to China, Russia, or India.

Part of me wondered if my ego were going out of control, but why not me? As a missionary, my great-great-great-grandfather Heber had opened England in 1837 and baptized thousands. Why couldn't I do the same in China or Russia? Maybe Heber would even guide me from the spirit world.

If I was in the ninety-ninth percentile of earthly intelligence, maybe my premortal self had been in the ninety-ninth percentile of spiritual intelligence. Dozens of times growing up, I'd been told God had reserved my generation to come forth as Mormons in the last days. We would fight the final battle before Christ returned and ushered in the Earth's 1,000-year sabbatical. Whenever my dad had gritted his teeth and asked, "Who do you think you are?" my unspoken answer was often, *One of God's most elite spirit children, reserved to come forth on the Earth at this momentous time in history.*

On the other hand, if I was born Mormon by my own premortal merit and choice, why did I have such a hard time with the religion here on Earth? Maybe something I'd loved about premortal Mormonism—or whatever we'd called it—wasn't manifest yet in the earthly church. Or maybe as a mortal I'd simply become a selfish, spoiled snob. Born into luxury and comfort, I couldn't imagine being a pioneer, polygamist, or dive-bomber. I'd been spoon-fed the truest, most complete religion, but I'd been a brat and spat it out.

Perhaps I could regain my premortal standing by excelling on my mission. I started praying for Gorbachev and his *glasnost* to miraculously open Russia to Mormonism. As an act of faith, I considered preemptively registering for a Russian class at the U. Whenever the phone rang, I wondered if Elder Maxwell's office were trying to reach me.

With my mission call looming, Tina and I strategized how our relationship could survive two years apart. We agreed everything depended on Tina's keeping busy while I was gone. She could attend college, volunteer at church and other charities, and socialize with church groups. In my mind, the separation would test whether Tina could obey Mormonism on her own. I still felt the religion was the only thing that could make her marriageable and keep her under control in the long term.

"Are you going to date while I'm gone?" I asked Tina. I struggled to imagine her dating without having sex.

She gave me a strange look. "I don't *want* to."

"Good, because we're practically engaged." *If not already married*, I thought.

"We *are* engaged," Tina said.

"I'll buy you a ring when I get back," I said, feeling mostly glad but also a little skeptical. So far, Tina had been trying to follow my example, but would she continue after I left? She'd started listening to classical music and reading scriptures. She'd gotten a normal hairstyle and some churchy clothes. We'd started attending religious lectures and the symphony. However, I could tell the transformation was stressing her out. Her ulcer was giving her more pain than ever.

One night, we started French kissing. As I sensed Tina getting aroused, I started freaking out about her sexual past and future. Later, I goaded her about falling in love with someone else while I was gone. She told me to stop being so self-righteous. *But what if I'm right?* I thought.

"I'd feel better if we promise not to French again," I said.

"Fine," she said. "You're the one who started it."

The next night, Tina and I wrestled on her waterbed, failing to obey my bishop's rule of three. Sometimes our tongues touched, but we quickly pulled them away. When I pinned her down one time, she murmured, "Trapped by the Mormon," and I fell into a laughing fit. Occasionally screened at the Blue Mouse, *Trapped by the Mormons* was a 1922 silent film about missionaries kidnapping British virgins to marry polygamists in Utah. Tina's quip was funny, but it also gave me pause. Was I foisting something unnecessarily strict on her?

I'd always thought "blue balls" was just a saying, but that night my testicles ached as I drove home. I wondered what Tina would do if I tried to have sex with her. Would she stop me, or would she allow it? If she wanted to keep me home from my mission, all she had to do was seduce me. If that happened, I hoped I could resist.

Reading about ancient Rome one night, I came across a description of bulimia. Tina hadn't mentioned hers in a while. Sometimes I wondered how accountable she was for her bulimia and nymphomania. Had she made wrong choices, or was it beyond her control due to abuse? Probably a mixture of both.

The next time I saw Tina, I asked how she was doing with bulimia. She admitted she'd already thrown up four times that day. I asked how she was going to stop, hoping she'd say by increasing her prayers, fasting, and faith. Maybe she could request a healing blessing to cure her bulimia, a miracle powerful enough to spiritually sustain us both during my two years away. However, Tina admitted she didn't know if she even wanted to stop. I couldn't believe it. How could she not see bulimia was evil? It was obviously a latter-day manifestation of the self-indulgence that had brought down Rome. Maybe Tina was too spiritually weak to marry someone in the ninety-ninth percentile. I wanted to go home and forget all about her.

Later, thinking about how the Romans fell, I could see why the mortal Earth's last days would indeed be final. Instead of

252   *   Christopher Kimball Bigelow

isolated civilizations rising and falling at different times around the Earth, now a planetwide civilization was forming. When it got overripe with corruption, the whole civilized world would fall at once like a big rotten fruit, destroying the planet and triggering Christ to come save it.

That night, I wrote: *I could be instrumental in warning people about evil's strategies in the last days. After all, I've been privy to some. Will I fight on the front right before the Second Coming happens? Or is my timing premature and the next generation will be even more valiant?*

Chapter 32

I STARTED READING EARLY APOSTLE PARLEY P. PRATT's *Key to the Science of Theology,* first published in 1855. It was one of the books Tina's dad had loaned me. "Your grandma Kimball loved that book," my mom said when she saw me reading it. I liked how Elder Pratt made theology sound scientific:

> *An intelligent being, in the image of God, possesses every organ, attribute, sense, sympathy, affection, of will, wisdom, love, power, and gift, which is possessed by God himself. But these are possessed by man in his rudimental state. These attributes are in embryo and are to be gradually developed. They resemble a bud—a germ, which gradually develops into bloom, and then, by progress, produces the mature fruit, after its own kind.*

While LSD was known for dissolving one's ego—which I didn't think ever quite happened to me—maybe LDS was sending me on the ultimate ego trip. Then again, I knew I could become godlike only by surrendering my will to God's. I liked thinking of God as the ultimate scientist. He understood and applied scientific laws on a higher level than humans could perceive, including seemingly nonphysical sciences like morality and the Holy Spirit.

As I absorbed Pratt's book, I wished Mormonism weren't so traditionally churchy, like a generic knockoff of mainstream Christianity. Why did we still use old-fashioned words like *sin, repent, gospel, God, salvation,* and *heaven*? I wished Mormonism said something more like, "Apply the scientific formula provided by our extraterrestrial parents, and keep progressing until you mature to their full-grown status." As a kid, I'd loved stuff like *Chariots of the Gods*, the idea that ancient earthly humans had received knowledge and technology from humanoid astronauts visiting from advanced interstellar civilizations. I could've dug Mormonism if it were presented more like that, along with cool supporting music, novels, and movies.

The Elder Maxwell sending had been phenomenal, but I wanted more supernatural experiences. I needed a closer relationship with the Holy Spirit, or whatever such advanced spiritual technology should be called. Elder Pratt's description made it sound better than any drug:

> *The gift of the Holy Ghost quickens all the intellectual faculties, increases, enlarges, expands and purifies all the natural passions and affections; and adapts them, by the gift of wisdom, to their lawful use. It inspires, develops, cultivates and matures all the fine-toned sympathies, joys, tastes, kindred feelings and affections of our nature. It inspires virtue, kindness, goodness, tenderness, gentleness and charity. It develops beauty of person, form and features. It tends to health, vigor, animation and social feeling. It develops and invigorates all the faculties of the physical and intellectual man.*

I thought I'd felt a little of what Pratt described, but I wanted to feel it deeper and oftener. Some Mormons sounded like they could detect exactly when the Holy Ghost came and went. Some talked like they conversed with the Holy Ghost in their head. Some testified the Spirit guided them even in mundane things, like one lady who claimed the Spirit helped her find the perfect statuette for her entry hall. Did other Mormons have spiritual brain receptors I didn't have?

Sometimes I felt an L-shaped tingle in my left cheek, and I wondered if that were the Holy Spirit. But the tingle also came while I was watching a worldly movie or making out with Tina, and surely the Spirit wouldn't endorse such things. Maybe I still wasn't living purely enough to discern the Holy Spirit. As I understood it, even the smallest thing could stand in the way— sleeping too much, drinking Coke, wasting time, failing to serve as much as possible, or letting my hand, tongue, or groin brush Tina too intimately.

On the other hand, maybe spiritual sendings were hard to pinpoint not because they were rare but because they were commonplace, often interweaving with my own thoughts and feelings. Maybe humans didn't realize how many sendings hit our brains each day, assuming every thought must be our own. If humans could broadcast messages via TV and radio, why couldn't light and dark spiritual powers transmit stuff directly into our heads? The more a person heeded the dark or light side, the more that side could influence him, making it feel like his own powerful needs and motivations. Maybe movements like hippies and punks sprouted up because the dark side executed a carefully planned worldwide campaign, whispering ideas simultaneously into thousands of spiritual ears.

I wished I could've seen spiritual reality from the get-go like so many in the church, but that was like wishing my eyes were brown instead of blue. I wondered if, given my personality and circumstances, I could've somehow borne down with enough faith and purity to get a spiritual experience while I was young, but I'd failed to do so. Would one unmistakable, undeniable sending have kept me on track, or would I have been like Laman and Lemuel in the Book of Mormon, rebelling even after seeing an angel?

One warm spring afternoon, I drove alone up to Mueller Park Canyon. I wanted to pray in the woods like Joseph Smith and see if I could trigger something bigger than the Elder Maxwell sending, maybe even a visitation by an actual extraterrestrial being. I was fasting, but I'd slept late to shorten my suffering.

Leaving the car, I chose a spot not far from where I'd first gotten drunk two years earlier. I spread a blanket, lay on my stomach, and wrote in my journal. After a while, I knelt and closed my eyes. Instead of bowing my head, I lifted my face to the sun. As I prayed, I could feel both outer and inner warmth. But then someone cleared his throat from the nearby trail, and I broke off, realizing I should've hiked higher.

After my mountainside attempt, I felt depressed. I wondered if I'd already been feeling the Holy Spirit for several weeks, and now it was withdrawing so I could recognize it by its absence. Or maybe I just felt down because my spring hay fever had begun and Tina and my family were irritating me. Tina had recently complained how phony and meaningless modeling was. I liked the money, but I hoped she'd give it up—it was bad for her worldliness and her bulimia. But then she was offered a weekend modeling gig in San Francisco, and she took it even though she knew I was against it.

Her trip fell on general conference weekend, when church satellites would beam out ten hours of talks by the prophet, apostles, and other general authorities. Growing up, I'd watched as little of conference as possible, but now I felt intrigued. When the first session started on Saturday morning, I joined the family in front of the TV, most of us still finishing breakfast in our pajamas. I missed Tina—she needed spiritual nourishment more than any of us.

The first speaker was the new prophet. As a teen, I hadn't liked apostle Ezra Taft Benson. He was from Idaho, and I found Idahoans even more backwardly vanilla than Utahans. His popishly massive turquoise ring bugged me. His wavering voice sounded strident and bossy, and he pronounced *Book of Mormon* "buck-a-mar-man." But now that I was religious and President Benson was the prophet, I listened. I hoped he would make a major announcement, like the opening of Russia or China to missionary work. However, he gave a regular doctrinal talk, with lots of Book of Mormon quotes.

"Wake from a deep sleep, yea, even from the sleep of hell." *Done that,* I thought.

"Ye shall clear away the bad according as the good shall grow until the good shall overcome the bad." *Done that too.*

"Put on the armor of righteousness. Shake off the chains with which ye are bound, and come forth out of obscurity, and arise from the dust." *Almost there, just need my mission call.*

When President Benson said the whole church was under condemnation for not using the Book of Mormon enough, I resolved to increase my study. I'd been skimming some parts and skipping others, especially passages in which prophets spoke in messianic riddles. I often itched to streamline and clarify the text, but then I'd remember Moroni's fears that future readers would mock their writings, which they'd had to etch onto metal plates. Some parts were cool, however, and I didn't think Joseph Smith could've fabricated such a big, complex book.

Then President Benson warned us against the sin of pride: "Pride is a 'my will' rather than 'thy will' approach to life. The opposite of pride is humbleness, meekness, submissiveness, or

258   ✳   *Christopher Kimball Bigelow*

teachableness. Pride does not look up to God and care about
what is right—it looks sideways to man and argues who is right.
Pride is characterized by 'What do I want out of life?' rather than
by 'What would God have me do with my life?' It is self-will as
opposed to God's will."

According to President Benson, pride was what had destroyed
the Western Hemisphere's previous civilizations, as documented
in the Book of Mormon. And the problem went even deeper
than that. "Was it not through pride that the devil became the
devil? Christ wanted to serve. The devil wanted to rule. Christ
wanted to bring men to where he was. The devil wanted to be
above men." I wondered why Lucifer was that way. Who did he
think he was?

On Saturday evening, my dad took my brother and me downtown to the domed tabernacle for the male-only priesthood session. Elder Maxwell kicked off the session. At first, I hoped for
another sending, but we were sitting too far away for eye contact.
Elder Maxwell's talk was full of deep cosmic stuff, how we were
chosen in premortal councils and how God organized number-
less planets like ours. While God was way ahead of us in progres-
sion, we were coeternal with him because intelligence and spirit
could not be created, only organized into progressively higher
forms, as with physical matter.

> *We were there before, when the morning stars sang
> together and the sons of God shouted for joy at the pros-
> pects of this stern but necessary mortal existence. Wonder
> is added to wonder as temples and scriptures tell us of still
> other worlds—of a universe drenched in divine design with,
> as it were, spiritual cousins in the cosmos. These plain and
> precious doctrines restored in our time through the Prophet
> Joseph Smith are pulsating with perspective and are so light
> intensive, like radioactive materials, that they must be han-
> dled with great care.*

When President Benson spoke again, I soaked up the familiar message, feeling my Mormon ego swell. "Young men of the Aaronic priesthood, you have been born at this time for a sacred and glorious purpose. It is not by chance that you have been reserved to come to Earth in this last dispensation of the fulness of times. Your birth at this particular time was foreordained in the eternities. You are to be the royal army of the Lord in the last days. You are youth of the noble birthright."

I believed it could be true, but I also saw why I sometimes had delusions of grandeur. At the same time, I was unsure what being in the Lord's army meant, beyond serving a two-year mission. Maybe my generation would be better than any previous generation at conforming to all corporate LDS rules and programs and all cultural Mormon expectations. But to me, that sounded like a robot army.

At home that night, I wondered about my mission. Had the Lord indeed foreordained me to go somewhere specific? Would the church get it right and send me there?

When midnight passed without Tina calling as promised from San Francisco, I gave in to paranoia, including shedding tears at one point. Maybe she'd hooked up with someone. Maybe she'd smoked weed or drunk wine. Maybe she didn't want to do church anymore. Maybe she just didn't like me anymore.

The next morning, I wasn't sure how much more general conference I could take. For the Sunday afternoon session, I retreated to my basement bedroom, turning on my little TV and crawling into bed. One of the apostles led what he called a solemn assembly. As he announced each priesthood quorum, all the men in that quorum stood up and raised their hands to sustain the new prophet. The apostle instructed people at home to participate too. When the Aaronic priests were called, I stood up in my tighty-whities and raised my hand to sustain the prophet.

"Ha," I heard from my bedroom doorway. My brother who'd wanted to stab me for smoking had snuck downstairs to see if I would conform. He smiled at me and ran back upstairs, and I knew he'd finally forgiven me.

Chapter 33

AS I DROVE TO PICK UP TINA AT THE AIRPORT, I STILL felt sour about her not calling me. She'd apologized the next morning, saying she was busy past midnight and didn't want to wake my family. I wanted to ask what she was doing so late, but I decided not to push it.

At the airport, Tina hopped in my car, kissed me, and gave me a teasing look. "Guess what," she said with exaggerated enthusiasm. "I'm giving a talk in church next Sunday. And I'm getting my patriarchal blessing!"

I knew what she was doing, but I still allowed it to work on me.

On Sunday, I attended Tina's ward. Her talk wasn't deep, but it was doctrinally sound and infused with her cute girlishness. On the day of Tina's blessing, the two of us fasted so her patriarch would be inspired. I hoped the blessing would reveal me as her future husband, saying something like, "You have already met your eternal mate, and he has blond hair." However, her blessing came out shorter than mine and less specific.

In the days after her blessing, Tina seemed depressed and irritable. She freaked out when I questioned her spending time with a male model, who'd offered to help her with her taxes. She said she was tired of paying for our dates, and she asked me to start repaying the $240 she'd loaned me. But I'd returned to the U full-time, so I was working even less often for my dad. My tab with him was almost $2,000, and my mission would add another $10,000. Tina had mentioned helping pay for my mission so we could marry with less debt, but now I wondered if she would.

One evening while I studied at my desk, Tina lay on my bed. I thought she was pondering scriptures, but then I heard a book slap shut. Turning, I saw Tina had been reading my journal.

"So you think you're better than me?" she asked.

"Not at all."

"Well, it *sounds* like you do." Tina's voice hitched.

"I'm sorry. I didn't mean it that way."

"I'm doing my best." She wiped her eyes.

"I'm just a self-righteous prick."

I started hiding my notebook so I could keep being honest. That night, I wrote: *Tina and I have been having a hard time. I'm quickly progressing, and she's holding back or failing to keep up. Sometimes I lecture her, but she won't acknowledge anything I've said.*

"Remember your age difference," my mom advised me. "You're almost twenty. She's still only seventeen. Your mission will give her a chance to grow up."

In early May 1986, only two months after I'd first seen the bishop, I submitted my mission application. I fasted to make sure the apostles felt inspired about my call. I'd intended to fast for forty-eight hours, but I woke up the second day feeling too weak and nauseated to continue.

With my mission papers submitted, I felt strangely antsy, as if the dark side were working harder on me. I couldn't bring myself to read much for school or church. Sometimes I let myself think like an atheist, but within half an hour I'd always feel cold and clammy. Tina and I fell back into French kissing, and our waterbed wrestling increased until one time I climaxed in my jeans, which I hadn't realized could happen. Technically we hadn't broken any necking and petting rules, but I wondered if I should tell the bishop. I decided not to, as the climax had been an involuntary response, like a nocturnal emission while I was awake.

Arriving home from the U one afternoon, I opened the front door to find my way blocked by crisscrossing strands of multicolored yarn, like the web of a giant psychedelic spider. As the family watched, I followed the yarn back and forth through the house. When I finally reached the end, I found a thick white envelope. As friends and family arrived, they made their predictions. My hands shook as I tore open the envelope and scanned the letter.

"Melbourne, Australia," I quavered.

Tina broke into tears. People whooped and clapped, relieved it wasn't someplace like Wyoming or Idaho. "It's pronounced Mel*bun*," an uncle called out.

"Hold on." I scowled at the letter. "It says Greek speaking. I must've done OK on the language test."

That set off another round of marveling. "Lots of Greeks down in Melbourne," my uncle said. I heard someone quip, "It's all Greek to me!"

I didn't adore the call, but I liked it. Australia seemed exotic enough, and it fulfilled my patriarch's revelation. However, part of me wondered if I were being shipped off to a spiritual penal colony, as far removed from Tina as possible. My Bigelow grandparents had lived in Sydney when my grandpa taught business at a university, and now they were living there again to serve as missionaries. The Aussies loved them because in World War II my grandpa had helped defend Australia against the Japanese. My grandparents loved Australia, but they hated living so far away.

Lying in my bed that night, I wondered if Elder Maxwell were sending me to Australia so I could master Greek, and then he'd transfer me to Greece as its first missionary. Maybe Elder Maxwell even knew where ancient scriptures lay buried in Greece, and he needed my help to retrieve them and translate them.

I would report to the missionary training center in two months. Before then, I would go through the temple and start wearing the sacred undergarments. Right before I departed, I would give a big farewell speech. I hoped I could wake everybody up from their white-daisy lives and warn them about the dark side's plans.

At the U, I ran into a non-Mormon friend from high school. He'd scored higher than me on the ACT, but he'd barely graduated with C's and D's. A transplant from the East Coast, he was a know-it-all fast talker, especially about Mormonism. As I told him about my mission call, he smirked at me and took easy potshots at Joseph Smith.

"If you ever want to get baptized, give me a call," I finally half-joked.

The guy's expression almost made me laugh, a mix of disgust, fear, and longing. I didn't think I'd ever see him again, but years later I'd encounter him with his teeth rotted out, his face pocked with sores, and his skin so thin his facial veins showed through. Eventually he'd end up in prison.

Another day, I tried to study on a couch at the U, but I fell asleep.

"Wake up," a gruff voice said.

It was Matt. I hadn't seen him in weeks. He'd invited me to his birthday party, but I hadn't gone. He sat down next to me, and I told him about my mission call.

"Australia will be cool," he said. "Maybe you'll convert Olivia

Newton-John or Mel Gibson or the man from Snowy River."

Skipping class, I gave Matt a ride to his new apartment downtown. As we sat on the familiar green sofa, I tried to describe my scary experience.

"You know what that sounds like?" Matt asked. "An acid flashback."

"It was nothing like acid, believe me," I said. "I didn't see anything. I just felt something—I don't know, from another dimension. Like a black hole trying to smush me."

"That sounds like acid talking." Matt shrugged and gave me a skeptical look.

For a moment, I wondered if I'd made a mistake. Had I let some weird little hallucination scare me back into Mormonism? But I knew it was real.

I missed Matt, but I didn't feel any desire to return to my old life. At the same time, I couldn't blame Matt. After his polygamous dad, how could he ever be religious? As a recovering cult member, he saw no real difference between mainstream and fundamental Mormonism. To him, my reconnecting with Mormonism was the same as if I'd joined his father's cult.

Each night, I tried to spend a full hour reading scriptures and writing in my journal. To keep myself awake longer, I sat at my desk. Before crawling into bed, I'd kneel and pray out loud for another half-hour.

"I think all that extra sleep you got was part of your healing," my mom said.

"My algebra class is helping too," I said. "I can feel new brain cells growing."

During family home evening one Monday, I proposed we all stop watching TV for one month. Some of the kids objected, but others said it might be smart. My dad agreed it would increase our spirituality. But when I looked at my mom, her eyes were red and teary.

"I'm sure it's the right thing," she said. "But how will I keep the kids entertained all day?"

My mom often watched TV while sewing clothes or folding laundry. She'd always loved the quiz show *Jeopardy,* which had been my first real word. When *Sesame Street* had debuted when I was three, she'd wondered, *How can parents compete with that?* But she'd still let us watch it every day.

I didn't attempt to enforce the TV ban. I'd taught the family correct principles, and now they needed to govern themselves, as Joseph Smith had said. Only my dad and I followed through, which was easy because neither of us watched much TV anyway. I felt inwardly relieved my lawful-good experiment had failed— such extremeness didn't sit well with my Libra personality. I disliked telling people what to do, but maybe my mission would make me better at it.

I thought about asking the family to give up Coke too, but I decided I couldn't do that to my mom.

One of my mom's brothers had a connection at a missionary outfitter called Mr. Mac. When the three of us met downtown at the ZCMI mall, Mr. Mac himself was there, recognizable from his TV ads. He smiled at us, but we could tell he was sad. The white-salamander bombing trial was all over the news, and one of the victims had been Mr. Mac's son, who'd died just a couple blocks away from the mall.

A salesman helped us assemble my missionary package. One blue suit and one gray suit, both with an extra pair of pants. Five short-sleeved white dress shirts, five long-sleeved. Black Sunday shoes and black walking shoes with rubber "Forward Thrust" soles. Seven neckties and seven pairs of identical black socks, so I wouldn't have to pair them. Umbrella, overcoat, shoeshine kit. White socks, white tie, and white pants for when I baptized people.

"Shouldn't I get some underwear?" I asked.

"Very funny," my mom said. It took me a moment to remember I'd soon be wearing temple garments. "But you will need these," she said, holding up a package of white handkerchiefs.

"Those are for old men," I said.

"Always keep a clean, ironed handkerchief in your pocket," my uncle said. "If the Holy Ghost makes someone cry, you can offer it to her." Giving me a gap-toothed smile, he picked up a small metal vial on a keychain. "And you'll need one of these."

I'd first noticed this vial while parking cars at Nino's. Unscrewing one, I'd hoped to find cocaine inside, but oil dribbled out. Now I realized the vial held consecrated olive oil for use in healing blessings.

My discounted missionary package came to $630. As I watched my mom pay with her credit card, I felt guilty. Most Mormon boys saved enough to cover at least part of their missions, but I was leaving in debt. At home, with new missionary gear in my closet, my spartan room smelled clean and leathery. I felt like a soldier prepping for basic training, followed by overseas deployment. I was psyched, but I knew I was in a honeymoon phase with the church. How hard would my mission be?

At church, someone said he knew a guy serving in Melbourne as a Greek-speaking missionary. "There's four of them," he told me. "The mission also has elders who speak Italian, Chinese, and—I think—Vietnamese. But he says he doesn't use his Greek much."

"How do you learn it, if you don't speak it?"

He shrugged. "I guess you'll find out."

Chapter 34

ONE EVENING, OUR MISSION-PREP CLASS SPLIT INTO twos and threes to practice door approaches. I already hated knocking on doors, having peddled Scout-O-Rama tickets, newspaper subscriptions, Mason shoes, and other things. I dreaded knocking on tens of thousands of Australian doors to sell religion. I hadn't understood Mormonism until after LSD, so how could I expect Aussies to get it with just a few bland, processed lessons? I hoped the light side would guide us to the right houses and open people's minds.

A recently returned missionary accompanied me and another newbie. At the second house, a middle-aged woman answered. She looked Mormon with her short, frosted bouffant and garment hemlines visible under her pale-yellow blouse. But she yelled, "Your church is a cult!" and slammed her door.

"Technically, there's some truth to that." Turning to us, the returned missionary seemed too ready with his response. "Every religion started as a cult. Mormonism was a cult of Christianity, just as Christianity was a cult of Judaism. But we've certainly grown beyond cult."

The woman opened her door again. "That was so hard to do!" She wiped her eyes. "But you boys will get used to it." Taking our hands, she pulled us inside for fresh-baked cookies.

I liked what the missionary class taught us about the mortal test, how it was designed to entice everyone toward both good and evil. We had to choose for ourselves, without Jehovah and Lucifer persuading us face to face, like they'd done in premortality. Here on Earth, fellow humans tried to recruit us to either side, and enticements entered our minds and hearts from both sides. As missionaries, we'd train people how to recognize God's spirit and follow its promptings, but I felt like I was still trying to learn how myself.

At the big church complex across from the U, I took a higher-level missionary class. The professor said his class would be an appetizer before our main course down at the missionary training center in Provo, where I'd spend two months learning the missionary discussions in Greek.

"What's the most fundamental doctrine?" the professor asked us one day. "If you had to sum up our religion in one sentence, what would it be?"

"Follow the prophet," someone said.

"That's certainly vital," the professor said. "But it doesn't give the whole picture."

Someone else raised his hand. "Faith, repentance, baptism, and the gift of the Holy Ghost."

"Another good answer. But think bigger."

"Keep all the commandments?"

"Endure to the end?"

"Love God, and love your neighbor as yourself?"

"Jesus is our savior," I called out, feeling certain I'd solved it.

"Nothing would be possible without the Savior," the professor said. "But he's a means to an end, not an end in himself, as most Christians think."

A woman said, "I am a child of God."

"Ah, yes, our most beloved children's song," said the professor. "That's the correct answer."

Walking over to his desk, the professor picked up a photocopied article streaked with yellow highlighter. "Here's what Joseph Smith said. 'God himself was once as we are now, and is an exalted man, and sits enthroned in yonder heavens. That is the great secret. If you were to see him today, you would see him like a man in form, like yourselves. God himself, the Father of us all, dwelt on an earth.'"

"I wish that was in the scriptures," a guy commented.

"I agree," said the professor. "Now here's the other side of the coin." He looked down at the article again. "'We must learn how to be gods ourselves, to be kings and priests to God, the same as all gods have done before us. We do it by going from one small degree to another, and from a small capacity to a great one, from grace to grace, from exaltation to exaltation. We inherit the same power, the same glory, and the same exaltation, until we arrive at the station of a god and ascend the throne of eternal power.'"

"I hope we can teach this stuff," I said.

Thumbing his chin, the professor looked at me. "We have to be careful. Other Christians think it's blasphemous. They think heaven means sitting around on clouds, strumming harps and praising God. But to me, that's what sounds blasphemous, that God would put us through so much just so we can praise him. The real way to serve God is to become like him and expand his works."

As the discussion continued, I didn't see how anyone could resist such logical doctrine. Why else would God create this world, allow it to go feral, and then test his offspring here? Nothing less than our own potential godhood was worth it. If I could express this compellingly enough, the smartest Aussies would eat it up. Mormonism was like the gifted program of Christianity. If missionaries sought people in the spiritual ninety-ninth percentile and Australia had sixteen million people, then it should have

160,000 Mormons, but it didn't have even half that yet. Maybe I could do for Australia what Heber had done for England, baptizing hundreds. Most would plateau in a lesser degree of glory, but some would eventually populate entire galaxies with their own spirit-children.

I wondered what God had been like in his embryonic human stage. All humans sinned, so how much had he sinned before he repented? I knew he couldn't have been a murderer, because murderers couldn't be exalted to full godhood. But he might've been a thief or even an adulterer before he'd repented. If that weren't possible, then Mormon theology wasn't true. If anyone said people like Tina and me couldn't eventually become as pure and powerful as God, they were denying Christ's atonement.

I remembered something I'd read in my Norton literature anthology. Mark Twain hadn't liked the Mormons, but in *Letters from the Earth*, he'd unknowingly preached Mormon theology. Mingling among humans as an undercover observer, Twain's archangel reported: "From youth to middle age, all men and women prize copulation above all other pleasures combined, yet it is not in their heaven." But in reality, archangels could "continue the act and its supremest ecstasies unbroken and without withdrawal for centuries." I hoped I could tell Aussies about eternal sex for those who attained godhood—it seemed like a major selling point, especially compared to other Christian religions.

As practice for my farewell talk, I bore my testimony in sacrament meeting. Coming down from the pulpit, I felt light and happy, like I'd just been baptized or something. That evening in the basement, I sensed the spiritual veil wavering and the dark side drawing near. I felt snarling voices in my head, but they didn't say anything intelligible. I went upstairs and sat with my dad, later returning to bed and praying until I felt peaceful. In my journal, I half-jokingly wrote: *I wish the Lord showed as much interest in me as Satan does.*

Driving up Bountiful's Fifth South one afternoon, I saw a transient man standing on a street corner, watching traffic go by. When I passed close enough for eye contact, the man gave me a challenging look, as if daring me to help him. I didn't have extra money, so I hoped someone else would stop. Continuing up into the foothills, I wondered if the man were an otherworldly being in disguise, perhaps one of the Three Nephites. Maybe he was testing the Mormons of Bountiful to see how much charity we had. If so, I'd failed, but at least I was starting to think beyond chaotic neutrality.

I wanted to see extraterrestrial beings like my mom occasionally did. Before a surgery, when my grandpa LaVell's five sons gave him a blessing, my mom saw LaVell's twin sons standing in the circle as adult spirits. Born prematurely just four years before me, they'd died within hours. Another time, a trio of early Mormon leaders appeared to my mom to thank the family for supporting LeRoy's restoration of Nauvoo. Some of the children, including my mom, had felt neglected when Roy and Marge spent so much time in Nauvoo. Most recently, my mom had seen a thin, ghastly demoness hovering over one of my sisters who was struggling with bulimia.

One night while praying, I asked that I might better know Jesus Christ, even face to face. I felt a strong spiritual feeling that kept growing, but then I lost my nerve and blocked the feeling. It seemed somehow too intimate to meet the Savior or even just an angel. Visitations often triggered obligations or trials—it seemed like all the early Mormons who'd seen an angel ended up tarred and feathered or something. I didn't want to bring anything like that upon myself. I could wait until the afterlife to meet glorified beings.

☯

On June 15, 1986, my dad ordained me to the Melchizedek priesthood, the same power God held, different only in degree. When we got home, he handed me a card showing our line of priesthood authority from man to man, all the way back to Jesus Christ. Now that I held the higher priesthood, I almost wanted the dark side to come at me again, so I could rebuke it and cast it out.

We filled my keychain vial with consecrated olive oil. It wasn't a magic cane, cloak, stone, rod, or scroll, but I was now carrying around a spiritual first aid kit. If I came upon a car accident, I could lay my hands on an injured person's head, anoint them, and command them to live, if the Holy Spirit confirmed it was God's will.

Soon my parents would take me to the Salt Lake Temple to receive my endowment. I'd been to the temple twice before, but only to perform baptisms for the dead in the basement. Teens couldn't go upstairs until they were called on a mission or getting sealed to a spouse. As I'd waited in my white jumpsuit, I couldn't resist looking around for spirits. I'd heard about people seeing rows of spirits queued up for baptism. As a mortal was vicariously immersed in each spirit's name, a smile crossed the spirit's face and it disappeared.

When I was little, I'd thought worldly people had sex in beds but Mormons did it inside the temple. That was why sex and the temple were both so secret and sacred. At first, I'd assumed sex happened only once for Mormons, right after their temple sealing. I'd pictured a new couple contorted over a toilet in a temple restroom. The woman's dress was hitched up, and the man's pants were pulled down to his knees. To brace herself, the woman gripped the nearby toilet-paper dispenser. I could see her red-painted fingernails digging into the white, squeezably soft roll.

Later, I realized sex must happen at least once for each child. Sometimes my parents hired a sitter and dressed up to attend the big white temple on Santa Monica Boulevard, near Beverly Hills. On those evenings, I felt a weird energy in the house. My parents seemed like a couple sneaking away on a romantic tryst. I figured their small suitcases must hold some kind of holy white lingerie. However, they went to the temple a lot more often than my mom got pregnant.

When I was in fifth grade, my dad took me to school one evening for sex education. Back home in the garage, we'd stayed in the car talking. The film had said masturbation was normal and healthy, but my dad told me Mormons didn't believe in it. I wondered how I'd know when my body was ripe enough to try it. Before long, the garage door's automatic light clicked off, and we sat in total darkness.

"When you're married," I asked, "how often does sex happen?"

My dad paused, and I wondered if he were giving me a weird look in the dark. "Probably once or twice a week," he finally said.

I was shocked. My parents didn't attend the temple anywhere near that often. The next day after school, I snuck into my parents' bedroom. Snooping through bedside drawers, I found a small, flimsy, flesh-colored bowl. Was it used in a secret sex ritual? Lifting the bedclothes, I checked for a rubber sheet. Some of my bed-wetting siblings had rubber sheets on their beds, but my parents did not. I wondered how a male could tell which fluid he was squirting—I couldn't imagine anything more embarrassing than accidentally injecting urine into a female. Either way, sex must soak people's beds.

If Mormons mated at home rather than in the temple, their white temple undergarments must have something to do with it. My mom didn't expose her garments beyond the master bedroom suite, but sometimes my dad came downstairs in his. Garments looked like a white, silky, short-sleeved jumpsuit with flaps, slits, and seams over private areas. A few spots looked handstitched, as if my mom had mended small rips.

Sometimes my parents had half-jokingly kept their temple plans secret, so evil spirits wouldn't overhear and try to thwart them. As I got older, my mom teased me about the temple. "I'm too tired to climb all those ladders tonight," she'd say before they left. "A spark singed my dress," she'd say after they got home. "The worker pricked my toe too hard." "Your dad brought the wrong size of rope."

Chapter 35

ON OUR WAY DOWNTOWN TO THE TEMPLE, I WONDERED if I'd experience anything supernatural inside. Maybe that was the real reason they kept the temple so secret. Outside the temple, adults couldn't discuss the temple's visions and visitations, not even with their own children.

"My first time through," my mom told me, "I felt uncomfortable until I made eye contact with my dad. He winked at me, and then I felt just fine. I knew if he thought it was legit, then it must be legit."

The strangest part came at the beginning, but I liked it. In a private cubicle, I hung up my new missionary clothes and slid off my old white underpants, preparing to exchange holey for holy. Like a patient in some kind of spiritual hospital, I pulled a white poncho over my head, which covered me down to my knees. Then some temple workers led me into a nearby chamber for my washing and anointing.

"Don't worry," my dad whispered, "no one will see your nakedness."

As I walked, the marble floor felt cold on my bare feet, and cool air flowed up my body. I wasn't worried. Nothing too kinky was going to happen—or if it did, it would be OK because I fully trusted Mormonism.

When an elderly worker reached through the side of my poncho, I felt a moment of alarm—it'd been only a few months since my last chicken-hawk ambush. But all the worker did was dab water on a few spots from my head to my feet and pronounce some blessings. When he got to my "loins," he touched the outside of my hip. After the water, he repeated everything with olive oil, which I felt grateful didn't come from a Crisco-like tin.

The blessings said I could be cleansed of "the blood and sins of this generation" and become a ruler in God's kingdom. It was my potential, not a guarantee—I still had to prove myself by following Christ. Only a few people, such as my Kimball grandparents, received an additional ordinance that made their calling and election sure, guaranteeing their eventual godhood.

At the end of the ritual, I pulled on some garments. Now I would wear them day and night for the rest of my life, removing them only for showers, sports, or sex. The salesclerk had wanted me to try the new two-piece garments. "That's what all the young people get," she said. But two-piece garments didn't seem different enough from worldly underwear—they just looked like an undershirt and boxer-briefs. Instead, I chose the one-piece jumpsuit style, like my parents wore.

"You grandfather was the same way," my mom had said in the car. "He grew up with garments to the wrists and ankles. When the short ones came out, he was not impressed." In Australia, other missionaries would call me "one-piece Bigelow."

After my washing and anointing, they took me to a theater room to receive my endowment. They put my dad and me on the front row, with other newbies and their escorts. As I sat waiting, I thought of the temple's six-foot-thick granite walls protecting me from all the wickedness just outside.

Acted out by elderly temple workers, the endowment told the story of the Earth's creation and how the devil had persuaded Adam and Eve to fall. When I heard how our planet was made from "matter unorganized," I pictured a Jackson Pollack painting. I liked how Adam and Eve were heroes, not villains.

Adam would've stayed innocent in Eden forever, but Eve made the hard choice so humanity could go through the mortal test. The endowment rigmarole included standing, making gestures, clasping hands, repeating lines, and rearranging our white robes and other accessories. Speaking in unison, we made covenants to obey God so we could eventually become celestial royalty, which sounded completely cool to me.

Some things about the endowment bugged me. The story felt disjointed in places. The premortal Jesus Christ, called Jehovah, played a low-key role—the endowment mentioned his gospel and atonement, but he was mostly just a middleman between God and Adam. At times, the ritual felt robotic or even cultish, like when we all bowed our heads and said yes or when we ran our thumbs across our throats and bellies to mime slitting them open. However, I liked the portrayal of Satan, who dared rebel right to God's face. He bragged about having his own priesthood powers, which I assumed meant the occult.

When Satan got cast out, I paid close attention to how the apostle characters did it. I thought of the *Monster Manual* description of a satanic figure called Asmodeus. Thirteen feet tall, he appeared ultra-handsome, with piercing red eyes, dark skin and hair, and small forehead horns. Drops of his blood could turn into new devils. In his true form, however, he was a giant serpent. According to Lynn Bryson, Satan looked like any other pre-human spirit, but he'd become so powerful that if I did ever face him, it would probably turn out like Luke and the emperor. I felt glad the devil would never get a physical body.

After we passed through the veil into the plush celestial room, we hugged our family members. Sitting on a sofa fit for a king, I closed my eyes and basked in the spiritual sauna. As far as I knew, I hadn't seen or heard anything supernatural in the temple, but maybe that would come later. Overall, the experience had felt less weird than I'd expected—it was the same gospel, just more ritualized than at church.

In the locker room, as my dad and I changed out of our temple whites, I felt like a just-returned astronaut going through decompression. I noticed my dad's Elvis-style polyester jumpsuit with its gigantic, winged collar was starting to yellow.

"Now *that's* religion," my dad said over the cubicle wall.

"Yep." I really hoped I could keep all the covenants well enough to return to God's presence and receive all the rewards.

On our way out, I chucked my dingy, skimpy underpants in the trash.

With only a few weeks left before I entered the missionary training center, I attended several more endowment sessions with my parents or friends from mission prep. Taking the freeway south to a newer temple, where I preferred the endowment's filmed version, I got pulled over for speeding. The ticket put me over the point limit, so my driver's license got suspended. I couldn't believe my worst legal trouble had come after I'd turned good.

Inside the temple, I always felt warm and relaxed. However, the endowment was repetitive, and sometimes I dozed. One time, someone nudged me awake from behind, but when I looked back nobody was sitting behind me. I wondered if it had been the Holy Spirit, or maybe the spirit of the eighteenth-century Scandinavian whose name I'd been assigned. I wished Tina could attend the temple, but I knew she wasn't ready yet. She needed the temple's spiritual enlightenment and protection. We wouldn't survive as a couple without Mormonism to keep us both on track, especially her.

"You could make a goal to go through while I'm gone," I said.

She scowled. "I don't want to wear those things till I have to. I'll go through when you get back."

"Garments aren't so bad," I said. "These one-piecers keep my butt off the cold toilet seat."

Under my clothes, my nylon-mesh garments felt protective, like Bilbo's mithril undershirt. I'd heard stories of garments shielding people from flames or bullets. I didn't expect physical protection, but I expected spiritual protection. I'd hoped garments would ward off sexual temptation, but Tina and I were still wrestling too much.

I kept wondering about Satan. The dark side seemed like a vacuum that must be filled before the good side could progress. The mortal test required a devil, but it seemed unfair that someone had to fill such a role. Satan already knew how the struggle between good and evil had played out on other planets. He must've known he'd eventually lose his rebellion. Was he so angry that he was just going down in flames, taking along as many of us as he could? I wondered if some higher evil had tempted Satan or if he'd become evil on his own. Was there a galaxywide evil ruler on par with God?

Another thing I wondered was if Satan could ever repent, like Darth Vader finally had. Or could he be like Slugworth in *Willy Wonka & the Chocolate Factory?* That had been my favorite movie until *Star Wars*, and I liked it better as a movie than as a book. The movie version of Slugworth tried to get the kids to betray Wonka, but then Slugworth turned out to be Wonka's spy. Was Satan like that, God's spy pretending to be evil just to test us? I decided not—no one could fake the hate and anger I'd felt.

When I was young, I could watch *Willy Wonka* only once a year on broadcast TV, which added to its mystique. As I watched the videocassette now, the chocolate-waterfall room seemed like the Garden of Eden. The Oompa-Loompas were like Wonka's temple workers. My new-wave friends were Augustus Gloop, Violet Beauregarde, Veruca Salt, and Mike Teavee. Like Charlie Bucket, I'd made mistakes—I'd sampled the fizzy lifting drink and more. But in the end, my integrity had come through. "Forgive me for putting you through this," Wonka said to Charlie.

"I had to test you. And you passed the test. You won! The grand and glorious jackpot." I could imagine God saying something similar to me. Instead of a chocolate factory, the eventual jackpot would be my own galaxy.

Sometimes the temple reminded me of *Star Trek*. Some of the buildings even looked like starships, especially the newer temples. The movie version of the endowment showed people beaming up and down between heaven and Earth. In *Star Trek II: The Wrath of Khan*, humans figured out how to reorganize matter at the subatomic level and turn lifeless spheres into green, life-generating planets. However, Project Genesis had ultimately failed. Before being trusted with such powerful organizational science, humans first needed to master moral science and make temple covenants to obey and uphold it.

God and his spouse—or spouses—were advanced extraterrestrial beings who organized terrestrial planets and seeded their human offspring throughout the galaxy, so we could gain experience and progress to higher levels. Even Parley P. Pratt sometimes sounded like *Star Trek*:

> *God, angels, and men are all of one species, one race, one great family widely diffused among the planetary systems as colonies, kingdoms, nations, etc. The great distinguishing difference between one portion of this race and another consists in the varied grades of intelligence and purity, and also in the variety of spheres occupied by each, in the series of progressive being.*

I raced to finish reading the Book of Mormon before entering the missionary training center. It seemed like the least I could do, having failed to start learning Greek and master a few hymns on the piano. I'd already read the entire book once before, back when I was spiritually naïve. Early each morning, my family had read a chapter out loud. The religious parts were boring, but some parts were cool like a fantasy novel. I'd been fascinated by all the antichrists, sorcerers, assassins, and cannibals.

One hero chopped off dozens of enemy arms. Even after his head was cut off, one bad guy tried to suck air through his blood-gurgling windpipe. Slain warriors filled entire Amazon-sized rivers. Countless human bones lay scattered across wildernesses. People got burned alive or buried under collapsing buildings. Whole cities sank into the ocean or disappeared under mountains. In between wars and disasters, the people fell into political intrigues and secret combinations. I'd often fantasized about starting a band of modern-day Gadianton Robbers, hiding out in mountain caves above Bountiful.

Rereading the Book of Mormon from my new perspective, I realized the dark side had been grooming me to become an antichrist like Nehor, Korihor, or Sherem. In addition, I found myself worrying about America. I'd been taught that Mormonism was the religious component of the American Revolution, delayed a few years to ensure separation of church and state. After their deaths, several Founding Fathers had appeared to a Mormon prophet and requested baptism by proxy. But in the 1960s, America started drifting into the same antireligious vortex that had sucked down two Book of Mormon civilizations. When the majority of Americans turned away from obeying at least the Ten Commandments, God would withdraw from this nation too. We'd divide into tribes, and when our infighting made us weak enough, other countries would invade. Maybe even an apocalypse like *The Stand* would happen.

I found it interesting that Nephites who'd turned godless became more hardened and ferocious than Lamanites who'd grown up heathen. Book of Mormon rebels often sounded like modern-day punks, wandering around with shaven heads and not doing anything productive. Chaotic neutrally, they took whatever food and valuables they could get. Chaotic evilly, they tried to bring down the entire Nephite civilization. Eventually they succeeded, as antichristian rebels were sure to succeed again in the last days. I felt glad I hadn't stayed on the dark side long enough to become an antichrist, irredeemably hardened and ferocious.

I wondered if I'd ever seen any evil spirits without knowing it. I felt suspicious about the punk with the trained fly—I couldn't remember ever seeing him touch anyone or anything. And what about Buck, the cowboy sentry up in City Creek Canyon? I wished I'd tried shaking their hands to see if I could feel their flesh. I also wondered why I couldn't handle sexual anarchy. Logically, I'd thought it sounded cool to be a promiscuous bisexual. But apparently I was a monogamist heterosexual by nature. For me, it was a gut-level instinct. Was it biological? My upbringing? Mormon brainwashing? Part of my premortal spiritual identity? I wondered how my friends could stand sexual chaos, especially Tina.

I wondered if I'd ever have such close friends again. During general conference, an apostle had called worldly friends shallow and selfish, but some of my friendships had gone deeper. I'd relied on them for so much, but we'd been like drowning people trying to rescue each other, especially Tina and me. Eventually, Matt would move to the West Coast, marry, have kids, and later find the courage to come out of the closet. Chad and Lucy would launch successful careers. Travis would get HIV but survive. Janet would have Vince's baby and become a San Francisco–based gypsy. However, Lisa would be diagnosed with schizophrenia and die young, probably a suicide. Lance would abandon himself to needle drugs, his parents not realizing he had AIDS until near the end, when carcinomas riddled his body. After having a child and getting arrested more than thirty times,

Maeve would be deported and end up in Germany, where she'd die from heart failure probably related to meth use, judging by her mugshots.

Whenever I went downtown, I felt more comfortable in the ZCMI mall's white yang than in the Crossroads mall's black yin. I'd stopped watching R-rated movies, but Tina and I still saw PG-13 movies. I felt guilty for enjoying the truancy romp *Ferris Bueller's Day Off,* but *Big Trouble in Little China* alarmed me. The movie portrayed a demonic, sorcerous underworld beneath San Francisco's Chinatown. I felt Hollywood's supernatural stories and special effects were conditioning people to accept real-life demons and sorcery in the 1990s.

One evening, I sat thinking alone in my dad's basement office. Why was I going on a mission, again? The dark side didn't want me to, so I knew it had to be right. Serving a mission was part of my repentance, like paying a two-year tithe on my twenty-year life. I wanted to serve the Lord and try to wake a few Australians to spiritual reality. But I knew what my deepest reason still was. If I served a valiant mission, the Lord would fix Tina so we could be together. On the other hand, I wondered if Tina were right for me. I'd helped her turn good, but did that mean we should marry? Maybe we shouldn't hold any claim on each other while I was gone. We'd been together on the good side for only a few months. It seemed unrealistic to think we could survive two years apart.

As I sat in the dark, a white flash suddenly went off nearby. At first, I thought one of the kids had sneaked down and taken a snapshot of me. But no one was there, and the burst of light hadn't seemed like a flashbulb—it was more defined and precise, with rays shooting out from a center. Could it have been a spiritual sending? I didn't feel any impressions in my mind. If the flash were a sign or an answer, I wasn't sure what it meant. I couldn't remember what I was thinking at the moment of the flash. Was the flash affirming I should stay committed to Tina or not?

I knew demons could send false sendings. They could even appear as angels of light. My understanding was that demons couldn't read my mind, but they could make educated guesses. Watching me brood in the dark, maybe a demon assumed I was confused or worried, so he'd tossed out a flash just to mix me up even more.

Chapter 36

BY THE WEEK OF MY FAREWELL, I'D WINNOWED ALL MY nonmissionary stuff into one medium-sized box. Besides some papers and mementoes, I saved a few normal clothes for when I got home. I loved feeling so streamlined.

I decided to read through my old papers and journals, looking for clues to my rebellion. In junior high, I'd written: *I like reading the scriptures. I'm thankful for Christ because of what he did. Mother made me a red shirt for Easter. She makes most of the family's clothes, which is a valuable thing.* After mentioning the Mount St. Helens eruption, the U.S. hostages in Iran, and the troubles between Russia and Afghanistan, I'd written: *I think it's all part of the prophecies. Times are troubled. These are definitely the last days.*

Even after I turned sixteen, I'd still written surprisingly favorable things about religion. *I've been ordained a priest and received my patriarchal blessing, which was wonderful. I baptized my brother smoothly and received many compliments. Getting baptized for the dead was an interesting experience. Our trip to Nauvoo was inspirational, a worthwhile change of pace. My favorite site was Carthage Jail, where Joseph Smith was martyred.*

Late in high school, angst had started to creep into my journal, as if I subconsciously knew risks and ordeals lay ahead. *I have a sense of unrest and anxiety about something I can't place my finger on.*

At the same time, I was getting sick of religion, especially the daily religion class, which I felt manipulated us emotionally and tried to make us think our feelings were the Holy Ghost. *I detest seminary, the people in it, and everything about it.* The last time I'd attended seminary, the teacher had asked me to stay after class. "I'm worried about you," he said when everyone was gone. "Are you involved in something you shouldn't be?" *Not yet,* I'd wanted to say.

After my first Maxim visit on May 11, 1984, I'd written: *It's a very liberal dance place in SLC where the clothes, hair, music, and dancing are new wave/punk and gays are allowed. Matt has been spending time with SLC punkers, getting drunk often, and maybe dabbling with homosexuality.*

To my surprise, I'd even written one small entry in the Cabbage Patch. I didn't remember taking my journal there. *Chad is a terrible party animal. He's one of the most morally unfounded people I've ever met. Yet I have become his friend. He has begun to escort me down to hell—* The entry broke off midsentence, as if Chad himself had just entered the Cabbage Patch. It didn't sound like the person I remembered being at that time.

The most unexpected document I found was my grandpa LaVell's transcript of the blessing my dad gave me on September 29, 1984, right before Matt and I moved to California. I'd never seen the transcript before, and I had no idea how it got among my papers.

> *This is a most exciting and wonderful time in your life. We commend you for your courage and integrity in doing what you feel is right for you. It is for your good, and we give you that knowledge through the power of the priesthood. We bless you that, through the agency you possess and the fine mind and talent you have been given as gifts, you will in fact make it good.*
>
> *We bless you that your trips and your activities will be safe from harm or accident. We challenge you and counsel you, as soon as you are ready, to take upon yourself the Melchizedek*

priesthood and go through the temple, so you might wear the holy garments that will protect you as you live faithfully. We bless you with health, that your body will withstand all the pressures and disease that can be put upon it.

You are well brought up, and you have wonderful habits. We counsel you to keep these habits and keep your body clean. We promise you with the power of the priesthood that your body will serve you well if you serve it well by obeying the natural laws the Lord has placed for you to follow. We commend you for your integrity to this point in obeying the Word of Wisdom and staying away from drugs, alcohol, and things that damage. Honor your body, for it is a great tabernacle and temple for your own spirit and for the spirit of the Lord, if you so desire it.

We know you are searching. We know you do not know the Lord at this point. We know you question the lifestyle around you. You see a lot of complacency and hypocrisy. You see a lot of unimaginative and lazy thinking of people who get in ruts and do not appreciate what they have. This is true of all walks of life, not just the Mormon religion or the Wasatch Front community. If you will be honest and open in your searching, you will find that there are human weaknesses everywhere. I think you know there is a God. We bear you testimony as we stand around you, through the priesthood, that there is a God. He knows you, he has spoken to you, and, if you are listening, he will continue to speak to you.

You are preparing yourself for great and marvelous things. We bless you with the power to remember the premortal existence, that your heart and your soul and your mind will be open to what you were before coming to this Earth, such that you will be able to appreciate the philosophies of men and understand and take the good that is there and not be duped by those who do not understand and appreciate the plan of salvation, the periods of preexistence, this short mortal life, and the great hereafter.

Search for truth. Be honest with yourself. Have integrity. Find that truth. Look for it, and be open to it, and use the fine standards you have been taught, not for religious reasons but for good common sense. Do the best you can. We bless you with continued ability to intellectually excel and to achieve. Learn how to work as you have done in the past. When you set your mind to it, you are an amazing and very accomplished worker. We bless you with the ability to be friends and to make friends, to learn to love and be loved.

We give you this blessing with all our love. We are your family. We have gone through much that you are going through. We appreciate what you are going through. We are excited for what you are going through. We challenge you to go through it honorably and with your heart and soul and mind lifted up, looking for the good in life.

I felt like I'd discovered an extra patriarchal blessing, even better than the first. I kept rereading one oddly worded sentence: *We bless you that your trips and your activities will be safe from harm or accident.* Could the Holy Spirit have inspired my dad to bless me about my acid trips? I wondered if LSD had been a forbidden but necessary fruit for me, the only way I could lose my spiritual innocence. Somewhere I'd read that *psychedelic* was a combination of the Greek words for "spirit" and "manifesting." Without LSD, I never would've perceived reality beyond the five human senses and understood the battle between spiritual darkness and light. Maybe I wasn't wrong to have taken LSD any more than Adam and Eve could be blamed for the dilemma God had put them in.

I wondered if LSD were inherently evil or just a neutral chemical. While I could imagine some gnarly wizard inventing

290 * Christopher Kimball Bigelow

the Ouija board with demonic help, LSD had come through a Swiss chemist, the epitome of objective neutrality. The hippies had turned LSD into a rebellious recreational drug, but what if a responsible church had embraced it too, creating the same chaotic/lawful dichotomy as druggies shooting heroin even as hospitals administered morphine? If LSD too easily opened the mind to the dark side's deceits, why not use it where the dark side couldn't reach? For example, if faithful, worthy people took LSD under prayerful guidance inside a temple, not too much or too often, could they understand more and make a stronger spiritual connection with the light side? Maybe LSD was part of the latter-day restoration, a spiritual medicine cleaner and safer than the fungi and cacti of old, but today's closedminded corporate church didn't yet comprehend it.

On the other hand, maybe taking LSD was just cheating compared to discovering spiritual reality through moral purity and faith. Perhaps LSD had shown me the dark side because that's all I'd merited. Or maybe LSD belonged solely to the dark side without any potential good use, although I doubted the dark side could commandeer chemical molecules like that. The evil spirits who'd provided my acid sendings had probably once been my premortal buddies, but then Lucifer had started his civil war, which was still going here on Earth. What had made my premortal friends take Lucifer's side? I'd been taught that fear was the main reason. Billions of spirits had decided the earthly mortal test with all conscious memory wiped was too risky. They'd believed Lucifer's promise to exalt them to godhood without such a difficult test, and now they were cast out with him. I wondered how tempted my premortal spirit had felt to join Lucifer's rebellion.

I could imagine my demons debating which revelation to give me while I was frying on acid:

"Let us tell him every living thing carries a fragment of God. The cosmic goal is to reunite into one essentiality that fills all space and time."

"No, nothing pseudo-religious. We do not want to nudge him anywhere near the enemy."

"Let us show him Lord Satan rules this world and he can share in the power."

"Remember how he fought against our lord before? He would never consciously join him."

"Then it must be atheism. Let us show him what humans truly are."

The thing was, even if the universe were populated only with randomly evolved life forms and not organized by higher powers, a human earthling couldn't know that. It was illogical to think LSD biologically released cosmic knowledge somehow buried in a human animal's brain. Without higher powers, how could such knowledge have gotten there? I felt proud I'd seen through the dark side's attempt to trick me. I could be egotistical, but at least I didn't think my human brain could perceive cosmic reality simply with some chemical help.

I wondered why I'd never experienced a bad trip. Maybe the demons had wanted to make sure I kept taking acid. In my experience, alcohol had been scarier than LSD. While I was blacked out, perhaps demons had controlled my body, but even then I'd been protected.

The day before my farewell speech at church, I fasted for inspiration. I'd wanted to use my farewell to reveal Satan's plans and call Mormons to action. I felt I had insider knowledge about the dark side's strategies. Now that I'd switched sides, I assumed the dark side would inspire someone else to spearhead the 1960s/1990s campaign. I needed to expose the dark side's plan and call for an equally compelling Mormon plan. As far as I could tell, the modern church was on autopilot, its only strategies just to keep sending out missionaries, building temples and meetinghouses, and pumping out processed, dumbed-down curriculum.

The night before my farewell talk, I gave up my grandiose fantasy and just hoped I could say something coherent, without my voice quavering too much. In the morning as I sat on the stand, the congregation looked packed, including the overflow seating. After my mom and sister played a piano duet of Pachelbel's Canon, which my mom had somehow made the theme of my return to Mormonism, I stood at the podium and told my conversion story, how I'd experienced the evil side's reality and learned its true motives, which drove me to join the good side. I wove in some scriptures and quotes by Joseph Smith and Parley P. Pratt. I tried to describe the dark side's attack, but I didn't say anything about my LSD sendings or my Elder Maxwell experience.

After the meeting, people waited in line to congratulate me. Tina, my mom, and the kids went straight home so they could put out refreshments for my open house. While I continued talking to people, my dad whispered he'd wait for me in the car. When I was finally able to leave, almost a thousand dollars filled my pockets.

As I went up an aisle, a man sitting alone in a center pew stood and waved me over. I walked up the row toward him, not recognizing him. He wore a brown suit, and he could've been anywhere from early thirties to late fifties. When I reached him, he gave me an earnest look and shook my hand with an odd emphasis, as if making sure I noticed the shake and would remember it.

"We are interested in you," he said, still squeezing my hand.

"Thanks," I said. I waited to see if he'd say more or hand me money, but he just nodded, let go of my hand, and moved away.

During the open house, Tina stayed near me. We kept giving each other pained, longing looks. More than once, she started crying while talking to someone, and the person hugged her. One time she glared at me as if I were purposely hurting her.

As I chatted with some Kimball cousins, my dad came up and clapped me on the shoulder. "He served a two-year mission for the devil, and now he's serving one for the Lord!"

At Tina's that night, I figured that since I was leaving in three days, we could French kiss one last time. Later, I felt bad as I drove home in semen-crusted garments. I'd been trying to avoid getting even any yellow drops on them. I figured I'd be stronger with Tina after I got home from my mission—that was when our proper temple courtship would happen. I hoped that if we could qualify for temple sealing, our righteous married sex would become way better than anything we'd experienced as fornicators.

Lying in the dark, I thought about the brown-suited stranger at my farewell. I wondered if he could've been John the Beloved or one of the Three Nephites. Why not? Surely something significant lay in my future, an important strategy the good side needed my help to execute, so why wouldn't an earthbound immortal connect with me, as at least one had presumably done with my grandpa LeRoy? When I got transferred to Greece, maybe I'd do some writing or something with John the Beloved. Maybe we'd perform some vital task together on the Greek isle of Patmos, where John had hid in a cave and written his freaky Book of Revelation.

The more I thought about the brown-suited stranger, the more I liked it. The Lord knew it was the perfect supernatural encounter for me, something I could see, hear, and touch but wasn't too intense. Like my experience with Elder Maxwell, it had happened inside a chapel, so I could feel confident it came from the good side.

Or was I imagining things? Could all my spiritual experiences be "the effect of a frenzied mind," as one Book of Mormon antichrist put it? Had LSD made me insane after all? I knew my mission would both test me and strengthen my faith. Out in the field, supernatural experiences would come to seem almost routine. I'd have encounters with both sides, receiving sendings about how to convert people and using priesthood power to combat evil spirits. I'd feel daily LSD-caliber spiritual impressions from the good side. *Knock on that door. Share this scripture. Skip that house—a serial killer lives there. Your companion has been alone too long in the bathroom.*

I worried about teaching Aussies the same processed basics that had never converted me. How could I get them to sense spiritual reality and start receiving their own sendings? Could I describe my own bass-ackwards conversion, or would I be forced to stick to the six official lessons, simply adding "I know these things are true"? I'd never received a recognizable sending until I took LSD, and I wished I could give Aussies a pill to similarly open their spiritual minds. If I hadn't been born Mormon, I couldn't imagine myself ever taking any interest in it. I supposed I'd need to find Aussies who were naturally more spiritual than I was.

On my departure day, my whole family drove the hour south to Provo. In the backseat of one car, Tina and I secretly clutched hands. We still considered ourselves engaged, and I wished I could've gotten her a ring.

As we passed downtown, the church's office tower looked like the cocoon of Mothra, a Godzilla-sized monster. Maybe the early church had been like a ravenous, roving larva, and now the church was in a dormant, defensive pupa stage. I hoped someday I'd see—perhaps even help—Mormonism break free of its corporate cocoon and emerge radically cool and different. I hoped Mormonism could be even more dynamic in the 2000s than it'd been in the 1800s. Little could I imagine I'd later work for six years inside the corporate cocoon.

I expected the missionary training center to be like a secure compound, with walls to keep in homesick missionaries and keep out lovesick girlfriends. However, the orange-bricked campus appeared open. I'd heard that spirit-warriors constantly surrounded the MTC, protecting missionaries from evil. Turning from my weeping womenfolk, I fell in with the other new recruits. Some looked grownup, but some looked like scrawny, pimply kids playing dress-up in their dads' clothes. I wondered how many had experienced anything supernatural like I had. I assumed most were just naturally spiritual, lawful-good boys who'd never questioned their upbringing.

As I let my Forward Thruster shoes carry me along, I felt psyched and spiritually buzzed but also leery. Earth life itself was a probationary exile, and now I was entering an exile within that exile. I wondered how much of a processed, white-shirt Mormon my mission would help me become and how many Australians—and possibly Greeks—I could bring along with me.

About the Author

CHRISTOPHER KIMBALL BIGELOW IS THE AUTHOR OF several books on Mormonism, including coauthoring *Mormonism For Dummies*. He served an LDS mission in Melbourne, Australia, and worked as an editor at the LDS church's *Ensign* magazine. His degrees include a BFA in writing, literature, and publishing from Emerson College, Boston, and an MA in creative writing from Brigham Young University. Bigelow cofounded and edited *Irreantum*, a Mormon literary magazine, and *The Sugar Beet*, a satirical Mormon news source. In addition to freelance writing, editing, and teaching, he runs Zarahemla Books, an alternative Mormon press. A Hodgkin's disease survivor and the oldest of ten, Bigelow lives with his wife and family in Provo, Utah. He can be reached at chrisbigelow@gmail.com.

CPSIA information can be obtained
at www.ICGtesting.com
Printed in the USA
FSHW011901290919
62511FS